MENSA®

MATHS GENIUS for KIDS

THIS IS A CARLTON BOOK

Text and puzzle content copyright © British Mensa Limited 1999
Design and artwork copyright © Carlton Books Limited 1999

This edition published by Carlton Books Limited 1999

A CIP catalogue for this book is available from the British
Library.

ISBN 1-85868-653-9

Editor: Tim Dedopulos
Design: Paul Messam
Production: Garry Lewis

Printed and bound in Italy

ALSO AVAILABLE IN THE MENSA SERIES

If you've enjoyed Mensa Mighty Mind Maze,
why not take a look at some of the other
books in the ground-breaking Mensa series.

Mensa Book of Total Genius *
by Josephine Fulton.
ISBN 1 85868 746 2. 224 pages.

Mensa Covert Challenge *
by David Colton.
ISBN 1 85868 745 4. 224 pages.

Mensa Ultimate Puzzle Challenge *
by Peter Jackson.
ISBN 1 85868 716 0. 304 pages.

Mensa Assess Your Personality
by Robert Allen.
ISBN 1 85868 468 4. 224 pages.

Mensa Challenge Your IQ
by Philip Carter, Ken Russell & John Bremner.
ISBN 1 85868 473 0. 224 pages.

Mensa Compendium of Conundrums
by Peter Jackson.
ISBN 1 85868 457 9. 224 pages.

Mensa Crosswords
by Philip Carter & Ken Russell.
ISBN 1 85868 447 1. 224 pages.

Mensa Lateral Thinking & Logical Deduction
by Dave Chatten & Carolyn Skitt.
ISBN 1 85868 472 2. 224 pages.

Mensa Mind Assault Course
by Dave Chatten & Carolyn Skitt.
ISBN 1 85868 467 6. 224 pages.

These Mensa books and many others are
available from all good bookshops, or they
may be ordered by telephone in the UK from
Books By Post on (01624) 675 137.

* Available August 1999.

MENSA®

MATHS GENIUS for KIDS

JOHN BREMNER

CARLTON

INTRODUCTION

Maths puzzles are probably a bad habit. I mean, people don't talk about enjoying maths puzzles do they? It's the sort of thing you do discreetly - like pigging a whole bar of fruit and nut chocolate when no one's around. This book is choc full, oops sorry, is very full of games, puzzles, hints, tricks, and other utterly crucial bits of mathmatical fun. And you don't have to be Einstein to take part. Come to think of it, it's just as well you aren't Einstein because he was rubbish at maths. Anyone can have a go at the stuff in this book. It's fun, it's fascinating AND it won't make you fat. What more can you ask?

All the puzzles and games are the work of my colleague John Bremner. John is a one man puzzle factory, and for a very good reason. He lives in Thurso. You probably live somewhere like Cheyenne, Wyoming, and don't know about Thurso. It's almost as far north as you can go in Scotland without getting your feet wet. And frozen. People in Thurso watch the aurora borealis instead of TV. There's a lot of time to think in Thurso, which may explain the compulsion to write puzzles and games. These are some of his best.

When you have finished the puzzles, games and other items in this book and are desperate for more, why not join Mensa? For details and a home test write to your nearest Mensa organization. British Mensa Limited is at Mensa House, St John's Square, Wolverhampton, WV2 4AH, England. American Mensa Ltd, 1229 Corporate Drive West, Arlington, TX 76006-6103, USA, or contact Mensa International, 15 The Ivories, 628 Northampton Street, London N1 2NY, England who will be happy to put you in touch with your own national Mensa.

R. P. Allen

Robert Allen,
Editorial Director of Mensa Publications

CONTENTS

PUZZLES

STARTER LEVEL PUZZLES

Puzzle 1

Which is the Odd One Out?

6 4 14 11 18

Puzzle 2

Two men take 30 minutes to plant 5 boxes of seedlings. How long would it take them if two extra men were recruited?

Puzzle 3

Which number should replace the question mark?

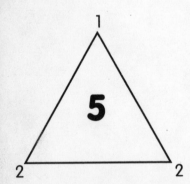 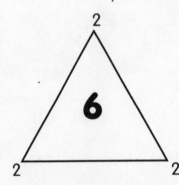 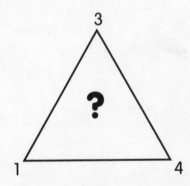

✔ *Turn to page 12 for the answers*

Puzzle 4

Which number should replace the question mark?

1 5 9 ? 17

Puzzle 5

Which number should replace the question mark?

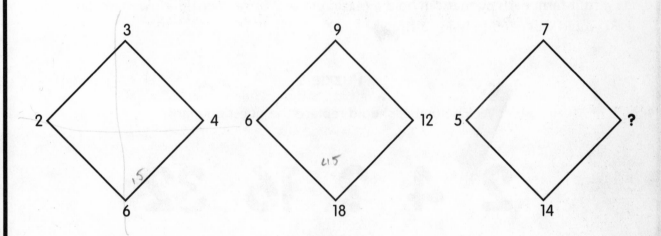

Puzzle 6

Which number should replace the question mark?

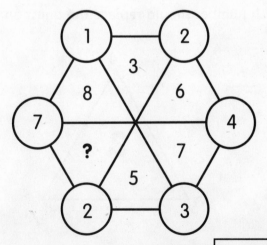

Turn to page 12 for the answers ✔

Puzzle 7

Which is the odd one out?

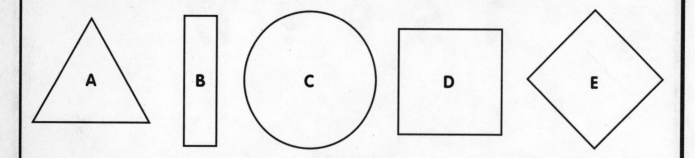

Puzzle 8

On a fruit farm each punnet can hold a maximum of 25 strawberries. How many punnets at least would you need to hold 53 strawberries?

Puzzle 9

Which number should replace the question mark?

2 4 ? 16 32

Puzzle 10

Which number should replace the question mark?

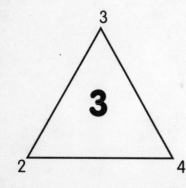 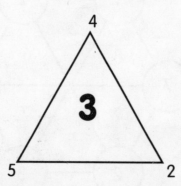 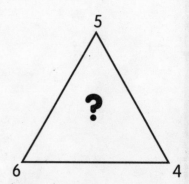

✔ *Turn to page 12 for the answers*

Puzzle 11

Which number should replace the question mark?

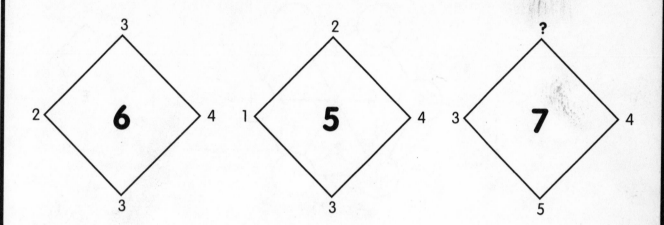

Puzzle 12

A boy takes 10 minutes to cycle to school. How long would it take him if he got stuck in very slow traffic and could only cycle at a 1/3 of his normal speed?

Puzzle 13

Which is the odd one out?

$^1/_2$ $^3/_6$ $^5/_{10}$ $^2/_4$ $^2/_3$

Puzzle 14

Which number should replace the question mark?

30 ? 20 15

Turn to page 12 for the answers ✔

Puzzle 15

Which number should replace the question mark?

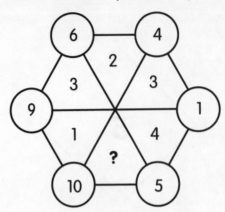

Puzzle 16

Which number goes into the blank egg?

10 + 5 − ? = 7

Puzzle 17

When you multiply two of the numbers in this circle together you get 30. What are the two numbers?

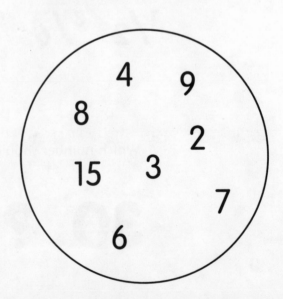

✔ Turn to page 12 for the answers

Puzzle 18

Which of these shapes is not symmetrical?

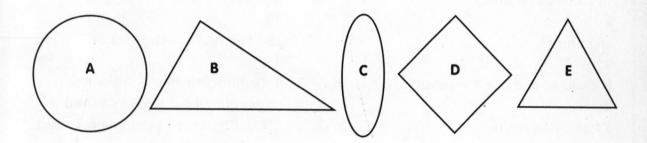

Puzzle 19

Which of these fractions in the largest?

$$\frac{7}{8} \quad \frac{2}{5} \quad \frac{3}{4} \quad \frac{1}{2} \quad \frac{1}{4}$$

Puzzle 20

I think of a number, add 4, and divide the result by 2, to end up with 3. What number did I think of?

Turn to page 12 for the answers ✓

STARTER LEVEL ANSWERS

1.
11 (Uneven number).

2.
15 minutes.

3.
8 (Add all and place in centre).

4.
13 (Add 4 each time).

5.
10 (The numbers at the right and bottom are doubles of the numbers on the opposite side).

6.
9 (Add numbers in two circles and put sum in nearest triangle).

7.
C (Other shapes have straight edges).

8.
3 punnets.

9.
8 (Each number is doubled).

10.
5 (Add bottom pair, subtract top).

11.
2 (The numbers on opposite sides add up to the number in the centre).

12.
30 minutes.

13.
2/3 (All the others equal 1/2).

14.
25 (Subtract 5 each time).

15.
5 (Subtract smaller number from larger number in two circles and place difference in triangle between them).

16.
8 (15 - 8 = 7).

17.
15 & 2 (15 x 2 = 30).

18.
B.

19.
7/8.

20.
2 (2 + 4 = 6, 6 / 2 = 3).

LEVEL ONE PUZZLES

Puzzle 1

When you add a number to 100 and reverse the answer you get 531.
What was the original number?

Puzzle 2

Fill in the blanks in this number square so that each row and column adds to 20.

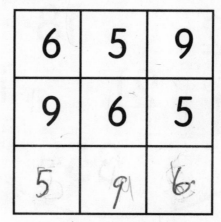

6	5	9
9	6	5
5	9	6

Puzzle 3

Fill in the blank hexagon with the appropriate number.

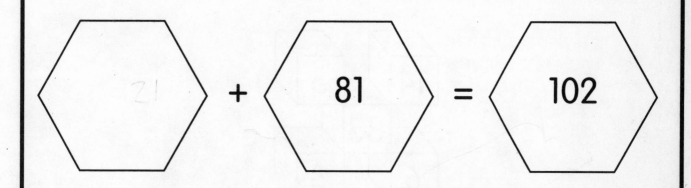

$$21 + 81 = 102$$

Turn to page 20 for the answers

Puzzle 4

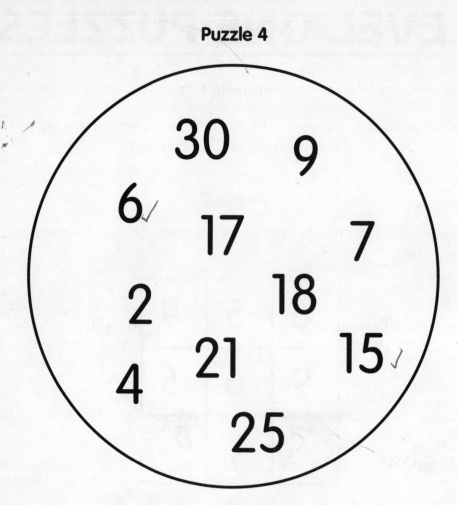

When you multiply two of the numbers in this circle together you get 90.
What are the two numbers?

Puzzle 5

What do you do with the corner numbers to get the number in the middle?

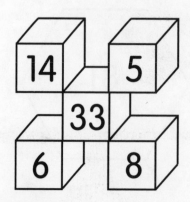

✔ *Turn to page 20 for the answers*

Puzzle 6

A man rode a horse to a place 10 miles away. When he got there he dismounted and took a bus home, leaving the horse to walk home on its own. How far did the horse walk home if it followed the track to get a drink on the way?

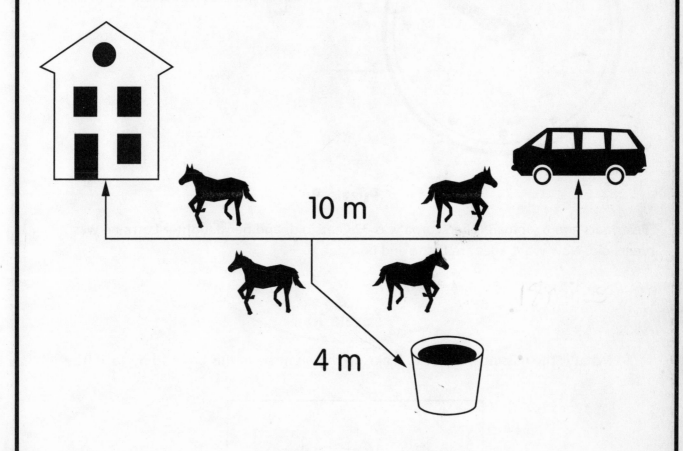

Puzzle 7

This system is in balance. How heavy is the blank weight?

Turn to page 20 for the answers

Puzzle 8

Here is a clock with a hand missing. Draw in the missing hand to make the time 10 past 7.

Puzzle 9

Five years ago a woman called Lorna was 32 years old, and her daughter Lorraine was 7 years old. Now what ages are Lorna and Lorraine?

37 12

Puzzle 10

What is the missing number to make all the numbers in this box add up to 100?

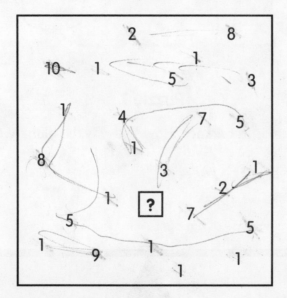

✔ *Turn to page 20 for the answers*

Puzzle 11

Which number should replace the question mark?

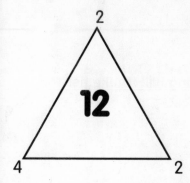 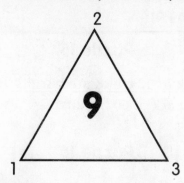 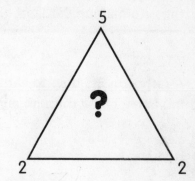

Puzzle 12

Which of these numbers is the odd one out?

14 56 35 21 33 ?

Puzzle 13

Which number should replace the question mark?

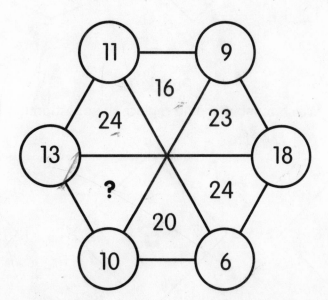

Turn to page 20 for the answers ✔

Puzzle 14

I think of a number, multiply it by 15 and then subtract 20 to get a result of 40. What was the original number I was thinking of?

Puzzle 15

A girl takes 3.5 days to eat a pack of 12 chocolate biscuits. How long will it take her to munch her way through a value pack of 60 biscuits?

Puzzle 16

Which is the next number in this series?

3   5   8   10   13   ?

Puzzle 17

Which shape is the odd one out?

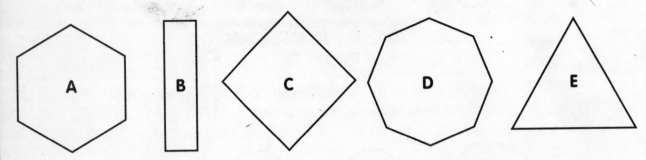

Puzzle 18

Which number should replace the question mark?

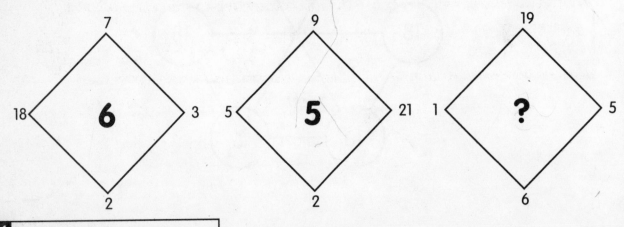

✔ *Turn to page 20 for the answers*

Puzzle 19

Which number should replace the question mark?

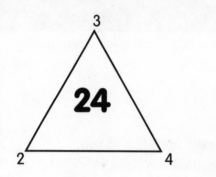
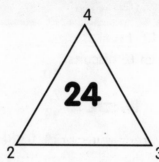
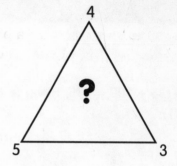

Puzzle 20

What is the missing number?

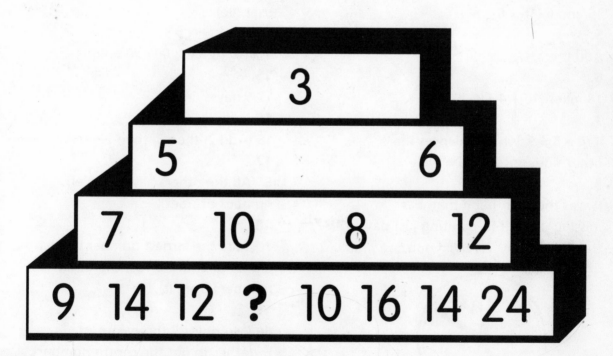

Turn to page 20 for the answers ✓

LEVEL ONE ANSWERS

1.
35 (35 + 100 = 135, Reverse 135 = 531).

2.

6	5	9
9	6	5
5	9	6

3.
21 (21 + 81 = 102).

4.
15 and 6 (15 x 6 = 90).

5.
Add them.

6.
18 miles (10 + 4 + 4).

7.
4 (4 + 5 = 9, which balances the other side, since 3 + 6 = 9).

8.
It was the hour hand that was missing. Here it is, pointing just past the position for 7.

9.
37 & 12 (32 + 5 = 37; 7 + 5 = 12).

10.
7.

11.
14 (Add bottom left and top, multiply by bottom right).

12.
33 (All the other can be divided by 7 without leaving a remainder).

13.
27 (Add numbers in two adjacent circles and place sum in opposite triangle).

14.
4 (4 x 15 = 60; 60 - 20 = 40).

15.
17.5 days.

16.
15 (Add 2, then 3, then 2, etc.).

17.
E (All the others have an even number of sides).

18.
7 (Take the largest number in each diamond and subtract the other numbers from it).

19.
60 (Multiply all three corners together to get the centre number).

20.
20 (Numbers to the left are 2 more than the one above, numbers to the right are double the one above. The ? is to the right of 10, 10 x 2 = 20).

LEVEL TWO PUZZLES

Puzzle 1

Insert the missing number.

1	3	5	7
3	9	15	21
9	27	45	63
27	81	135	

Puzzle 2

What number should replace the question mark?

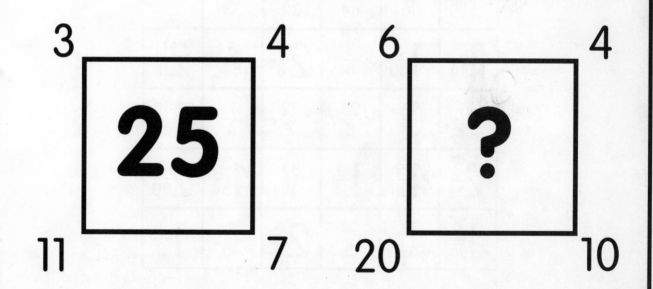

Turn to page 30 for the answers ✔

Puzzle 3

Using only numbers that have already been used in the grid below, fill in this number square to make each row, column, and long diagonal total 20.

8				1
	1			
		3		
	8			
6				2

Puzzle 4

Which two of these fractions add together to make 5?

$1\frac{7}{30}$	$\frac{43}{16}$	$\frac{20}{64}$	$\frac{19}{32}$	$\frac{16}{33}$	$\frac{55}{16}$
$1\frac{3}{16}$	$1\frac{5}{30}$	$\frac{3}{8}$	$2\frac{1}{8}$	$\frac{5}{64}$	$2\frac{11}{16}$
$\frac{16}{15}$	$\frac{18}{17}$	$\frac{27}{8}$	$\frac{22}{7}$	$\frac{7}{4}$	$1\frac{19}{15}$
$2\frac{3}{64}$	$4\frac{9}{18}$	$1\frac{1}{4}$	$\frac{33}{30}$	$4\frac{1}{64}$	$2\frac{8}{30}$
$1\frac{9}{16}$	$\frac{18}{64}$	$\frac{14}{5}$	$2\frac{13}{15}$	$\frac{3}{10}$	$1\frac{1}{2}$

✔ *Turn to page 30 for the answers*

Puzzle 5

What number should replace the question mark?

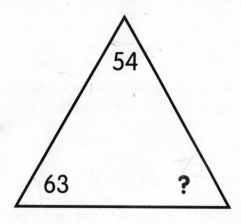

Puzzle 6

What number should replace the question mark?

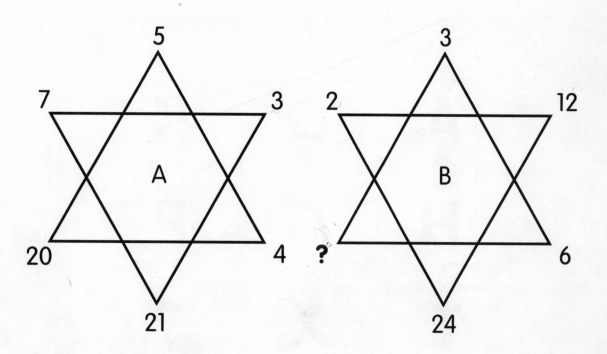

Turn to page 30 for the answers ✓

Puzzle 7

What number gives you 58 if you divide it by 5 and double the result?

Puzzle 8

Two cars are 50 units apart, heading towards each other. One is travelling at 30 units per hour and the other is travelling at 50 units per hour. How long will it be before they meet?

Puzzle 9

Jo said to Sarah, 'If I were your age I would be three times as old as I am now.' Sarah replied, 'If I were as old as you are now I'd have to wait 15 years to be half as old as I am now.' What are their ages?

Puzzle 10

The first two rows in each column give the third row. Can you work out the missing letter?

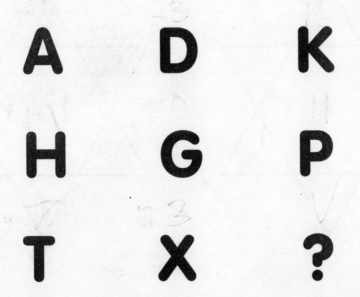

✔ *Turn to page 30 for the answers*

Puzzle 11

5+5 + 5 = 550

Add one straight line to make this equation true.

Puzzle 12

The letters of the alphabet have been numbered specially so that BONANZA èquals 105 and GRANDEE equals 112. What does GONZO equal?

Puzzle 13

An ant starts to walk around the edges of a die with 1cm sides. It walks as far as it can without ever retracing its steps. How far can it walk?

Puzzle 14

Frank started work at the Happy-Ever-After Cryogenic Rest Home. His boss carefully explained the exact temperature at which the system ran but Frank, being nervous on his first day, forgot whether the right temperature was in Celsius or Fahrenheit. Then, in a moment of inspiration, he thought to himself, 'Of course, it doesn't matter!' What was the correct temperature?

Puzzle 15

The following number represents a 9-letter word:

7-1-12-12-1-14-20-18-25
Using the same system:
20-18-25 is an attempt
7-1-12-12 is pure cheek
1-14-20 is an insect
What are the words?

Turn to page 31 for the answers

Puzzle 16

What is the missing number in the third square?

5   6
  5
3   2

3   8
  2
4   3

7   3
  ?
1   3

✔ **Turn to page 31 for the answers**

Puzzle 17
Move one matchstick to make this equation correct.

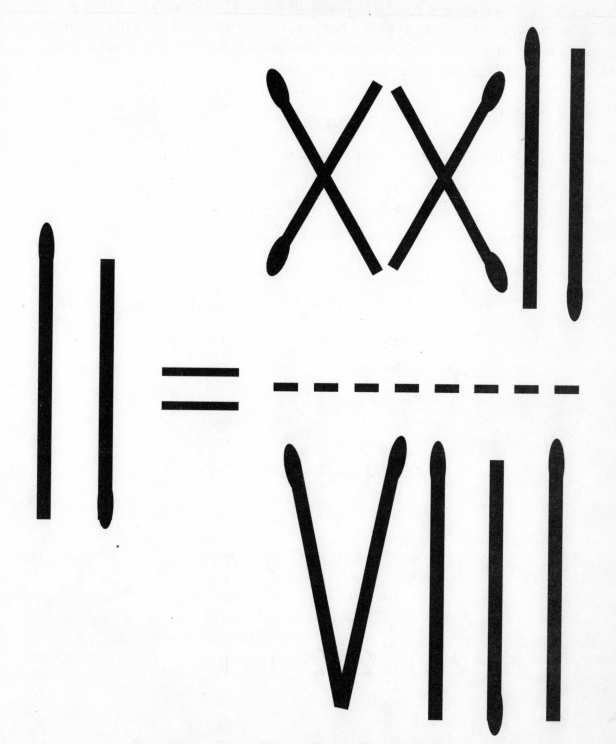

The answer will be all Greek to you!

Turn to page 31 for the answers

Puzzle 18

A woman cashed a cheque at her bank. The teller misread the pounds for pence and the pence for pounds. The woman, realizing her luck, quickly pocketed the extra money and bought something costing £1.52. The amount she had left from the extra was half the cheque's original value. What was the cheque's value?

Puzzle 19

Look carefully at this table. What is the next line?

```
1
1 1
2 1
1 2 1 1
1 1 1 2 2 1
3 1 2 2 1 1
? ? ? ? ? ? ? ?
```

✔ *Turn to page 31 for the answers*

Puzzle 20

Which number should go in the centre of the last triangle?

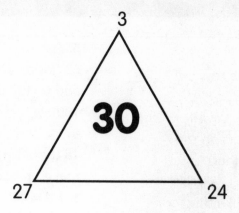

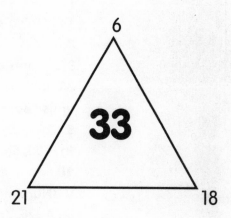

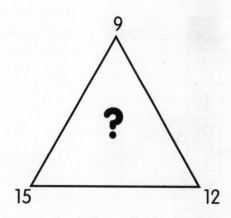

Turn to page 31 for the answers ✓

LEVEL TWO ANSWERS

1.

189 (Each row is 3 times the row above it).

2.

40 (The total of the numbers on the corners, when added together).

3.

The completed grid looks like this:

8	2	6	3	1
3	1	8	2	6
2	6	3	1	8
1	8	2	6	3
6	3	1	8	2

4.

The two corner elements add up to 5.

$1\frac{7}{30}$	$\frac{43}{16}$	$\frac{20}{64}$	$\frac{19}{32}$	$\frac{16}{33}$	$\frac{55}{16}$
$1\frac{3}{16}$	$1\frac{5}{30}$	$\frac{3}{8}$	$2\frac{1}{8}$	$\frac{5}{64}$	$2\frac{11}{16}$
$\frac{16}{15}$	$\frac{18}{17}$	$\frac{27}{8}$	$\frac{22}{7}$	$\frac{7}{4}$	$1\frac{19}{15}$
$2\frac{3}{64}$	$4\frac{9}{18}$	$1\frac{1}{4}$	$\frac{33}{30}$	$4\frac{1}{64}$	$2\frac{8}{30}$
$1\frac{9}{16}$	$\frac{18}{64}$	$\frac{14}{5}$	$2\frac{13}{15}$	$\frac{3}{10}$	$1\frac{1}{2}$

5.

63 (Inside angles of a triangle always add to 180 degrees, so 63 + 63 + 54 = 180).

6.

18 (Referring to the triangles which make up each star. In A, 7 x 3 = 21, 5 x 4 = 20; in B, 2 x 12 = 24, 3 x 6 = 18).

7.

145 (145/5 = 29, 29 x 2=58).

8.

37.5 minutes (The combined speed is 80 units per hour (50 + 30) thus, (50 units / 80) x 60 = 37.5).

9.

Jo is 30, Sarah is 90.

10.

V (Number the alphabet backwards, ie, A=26, Z=1, and subtract the value of row 2 from the value of row 1. Turn the resulting number back into a letter. K=15 and P=10, so the difference is V=5).

11.
Add a stroke to change the first + sign into a 4. Then you get 545 + 5 = 550.

12.
59 (The alphabet has been numbered from O = 1 upwards, so Z = 12, and then it follows round to A = 13, up to N = 26).

13.
9cms (The ant can travel all the way round the edges of one face (4 x 1cm), then back to the face behind it (1cm) which it can go all the way around again (4 x 1cm), but it cannot travel the three remaining edges without going over its own path).

14.
The only point at which the two scales are the same is -40 degrees.

15.
Gallantry, try, gall, ant.

16.
7 (Multiply top left and top right, divide by bottom right, then bottom left. Result goes in the middle).

17.
Move the final I of VIII and put it above the II to make the Greek letter pi.

18.
£36.56 (Which reversed is £56.36. She thus made £19.80 profit and after spending £1.52 had £18.28 left, which is half of £36.56).

19.
1-3-1-1-2-2-2-1 (Each line is a verbal description of the line above turned into numbers. Try reading them out – line two reads "One 1", line three reads "Two 1s", and so on, up to the final line, "One 3, One 1, Two 2s, Two 1s").

20.
36 (The series works in increments of 3. The trick is that the number increases across all three triangles, tops first, then back across the bottom row, and finally along through the centres. 33 + 3 = 36).

LEVEL THREE PUZZLES

Puzzle 1

If 2 is subtracted from both the top and bottom of a certain fraction whose top and bottom summed together total 7, its value becomes a half. What is the fraction?

Puzzle 2

What number should replace the question mark?

| 5 | 7 | 1 | 2 | 1 | 9 | 3 | ? |

Puzzle 3

What is the individual value of the spiders, birds, and horses below?

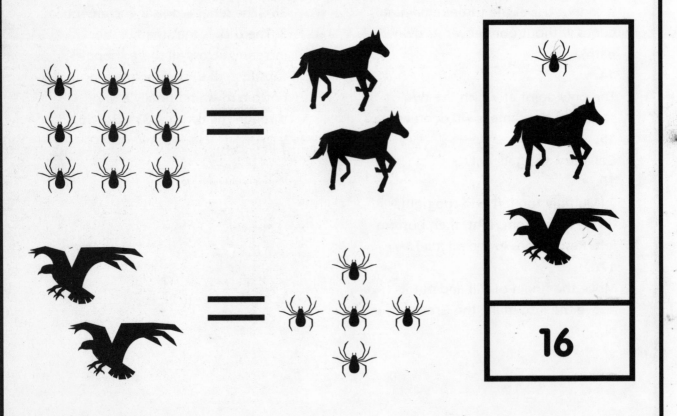

✔ Turn to page 38 for the answers

Puzzle 4

Insert the missing numbers in the circles, which, when added to the numbers in the other 3 circles attached to each square, will make the numbers in the middle.

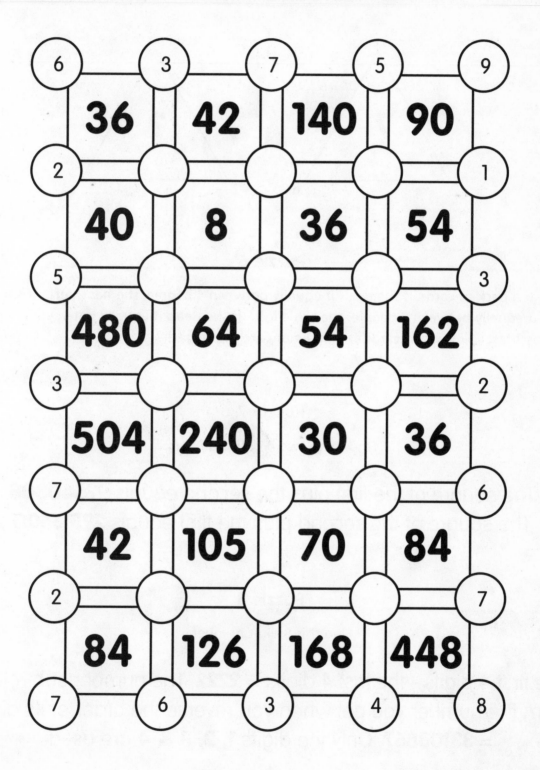

Turn to page 38 for the answers ✔

Puzzle 5

Insert the missing number.

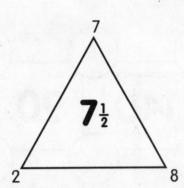 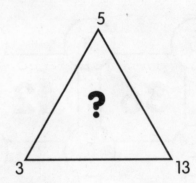

Puzzle 6

Jilly has a pack of cards. If she deals it equally between 4 people, she has 2 left. If she deals it equally between 7 people, she has 4 left. If she deals it equally between 3 people, she has 1 left. How many cards at a minimum are in the pack?

Puzzle 7

Find these two 4 digit numbers:

The square of the first plus the second equals **97540808**,
The square of the second plus the first equals **29516500**.

Puzzle 8

Find this 8 digit number:

The first 4 digits - the last 4 digits = **2222**. The number subtracted from the number you get when you reverse the order of its digits = **33108867**. Only the digits **1, 2, 3 & 4** are used.

✔ *Turn to page 38 for the answers*

Puzzle 9

Each like symbol is worth the same value. Fill in the missing total.

*	#	O	O	O
*	#	O	O	*
*	#	O	*	#
O	O	#	*	O
10	22	10	8	

Turn to page 38 for the answers ✔

Puzzle 10

Discover a four-figure number that is exactly four times greater
when the digits are reversed.

Puzzle 11

What is the fewest number of cuts required to divide a cake into eight equal parts?

Puzzle 12

You have a golf ball covered in glue. You want to stick other balls to it to form a cluster
which will stand upright on a table. What is the maximum number of balls you can have in
your cluster?

Puzzle 13

Find the next number in this series:

7   11   6   10   5   9   ?

Puzzle 14

What is the next number in this series?

11   13   17   19   23   ?

Puzzle 15

Complete this series:

4   8   9   27   16   64   25   ?

Puzzle 16

Remove 1 from the expression TWO ELEVEN to leave a dozen.

✔ Turn to page 38 for the answers

Puzzle 17

Which number should go in the centre of the last triangle?

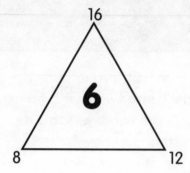 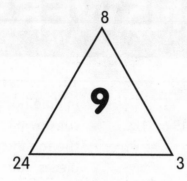 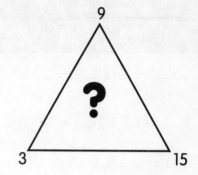

Puzzle 18

Which number comes next in the series?

1 3 4 7 9 10 13 ?

Puzzle 19

Which is the odd one out?

3 27 99 60 15 96 28

Puzzle 20

Which is the odd one out?

16 144 68 81 36 9 169 196 36

Turn to page 38 for the answers ✔

LEVEL THREE ANSWERS

1. 3/4 (3-2=1; 4-2=2).

2. 1 (5 + 7 = 12; 7 + 12 = 19; 12 + 19 = 31).

3. Horse = 9, spider = 2, bird = 5.

4. The completed grid is as follows:

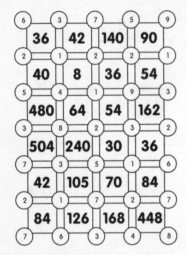

5. 6 (In the first example, 7 + 8 = 15; 15/2 = 7 1/2; In the second example, 5 + 13 = 18; 8/3 = 6).

6. 46 (46/4 = 11r2; 46/7=6r4; 46/3=12r10).

7. 9876 & 5432 (98762 = 97535376; 97535376 + 5432 = 97540808; 54322 = 29506624; 29506624 + 9876 = 29516500).

8. 44332211.

9. 12. (*=3; #=7; 0=1; thus 1+3+7+1=12).

10. 2178. (2178 x 4 = 8712).

11. 3 (First cut it in half through the middle horizontally into two layers, then cut down through the two layers to cut the top into quarters. You now have 8 pieces, four on top of each other).

12. 13 (You can stick 6 balls around the original one in the same plane, three above it, and three below, all in contact with the original ball).

13. 4 (Add four, subtract 5, and repeat).

14. 29 (They are the prime numbers).

15. 125 (The series is 2 squared, 2 cubed, 3 squared, 3 cubed, 4 squared, 4 cubed, 5 squared, then the missing number, 5 cubed).

16. Cross out the letters ONE (the only O, the second E and the only N) and you are left with TWELVE.

17. 5 (Multiply the two bottom numbers and divide by the top number. Place the result in centre of the triangle).

18. 15 (Add 2, 1, 3, 2, 1, 3, etc.; 13 + 2 = 15).

19. 28. All the other numbers are exactly divisible by 3.

20. 68. All the other numbers are squares.

GENIUS LEVEL FOUR PUZZLES

Puzzle 1

Which number comes next in this series?

192   147   108   75   ?

Puzzle 2

If

A = 25% of the value of B, **B = 1/5** of the value of C, **C = 71/2** times the value of D, and **D = 51**

what is the value of A?

Puzzle 3

A lump sum of 600 units is invested in a bank account. If at the time of the investment the interest rate is 4%, but for the first and third year the rate is increased by 1% and during the second and fourth year it is dropped by 1/4%, how much would be in the account at the end of four years?

Turn to page 46 for the answers ✔

Puzzle 4

Which number should replace the question mark?

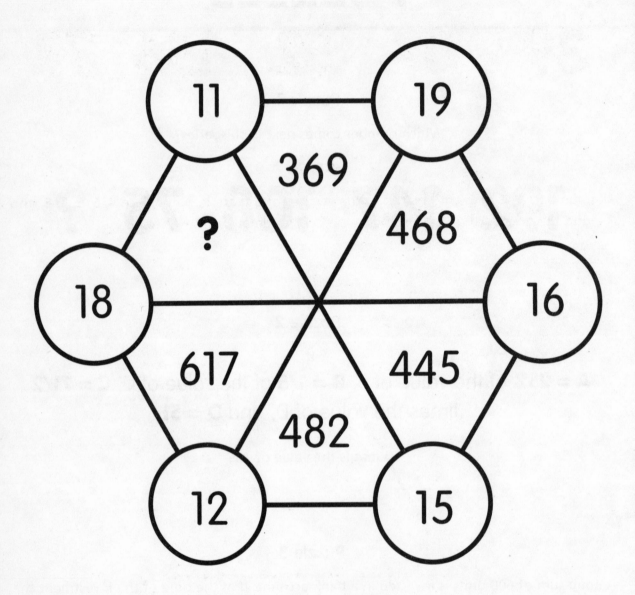

Puzzle 5

In a survey regarding the leisure activities of the population, out of a sample of 800, 27% admitted never to take any exercise at all. On the assumption that 25% of the remainder were lying, out of a sample of 5600, how many people would not take any exercise at all?

✔ *Turn to page 46 for the answers*

Puzzle 6

Which number is the odd one out?

39   117   52   156   78

Puzzle 7

The numbers 1, 2 and 3 are placed at the vertices of a triangle. Now place 4, 5, 6, 7, 8, and 9 along the sides so that the numbers along each side add up to 17.

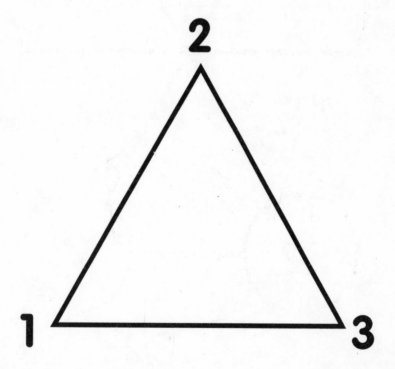

Puzzle 8

Given two numbers, if we subtract half the smaller number from each number, the result with the larger number is three times as large as the result with the smaller number. How many times is the larger number as large as the smaller number?

Turn to page 46 for the answers ✓

Puzzle 9

In a rectangular room, how do you arrange ten chairs along the walls so that there are an equal number of chairs along each wall?

✓ *Turn to page 46 for the answers*

Puzzle 10

What is the smallest number which:

When divided by **3**, gives a remainder of **1**, when divided by **4**, gives a remainder of **2**, when divided by **5**, gives a remainder of **3**, and when divided by **6**, gives a remainder of **4**.

Puzzle 11

Find a three-digit number which:

If you subtract **7** from it, the result is divisible by **7**, if you subtract **8**, divisible by **8**, and if you subtract **9**, divisible by **9**.

Puzzle 12

This problem was invented by Edouard Lucas, a French 19th century mathematician.

Every day at noon a ship leaves Le Havre for New York and another ship leaves New York for Le Havre. The trip lasts 7 days and 7 nights. Assuming the ships follow the same route each way but do not crash into each other, how many New York - Le Havre ships will the ship leaving Le Havre today meet during its journey to New York?

Puzzle 13

Three brothers shared 24 apples, each getting a number equal to his age 3 years before. The youngest one proposed a swap:

'I will keep only half the apples I got, and divide the rest between you two equally. But then the middle brother, keeping half his accumulated apples, must divide the rest equally between the oldest brother and me, and then the oldest brother must do the same.' They agreed. The result was that each ended up with 8 apples. How old were the brothers?

Turn to page 47 for the answers ✓

Puzzle 14

Draw 3 straight lines to divide this circle into 4 parts with a total value of 53.4 in each. The lines do not all start and finish on the circumference of the circle.

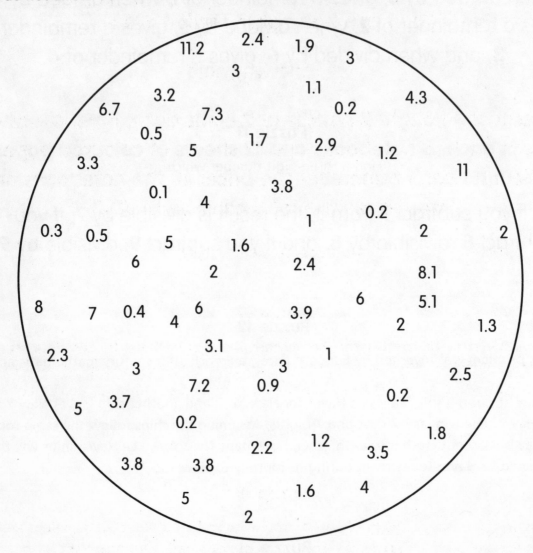

Puzzle 15

If you take a pair of 2s, you can construct two equations with the same value in which 'plus' can be replaced by 'times', like so:

$$2 + 2 = 2 \times 2.$$

You can also do it with three numbers, like so:

$$1 + 2 + 3 = 1 \times 2 \times 3.$$

Can you do it with four numbers? They don't need to all be different.

✔ Turn to page 47 for the answers

Puzzle 16

'The total comes to $1.70,' said the shop assistant.

'That can't be right,' replied Suzy.

'Oh, and why not?'

'Because I bought 2 pencils at 2 cents each, 5 pencils at 4 cents each, 8 notebooks and 12 sheets of coloured paper. Although I can't remember the prices of the notebooks and the paper, the total can't be $1.70.'

$8a + 12b = 146$

$4a + 6b = 73$

How does Suzy know that?

Puzzle 17

Cathy takes in stray kittens (whether her mother likes it or not). Her friends tease her about this, so she's sensitive about just how many stray kittens she's adopted. All she'll say when asked is: 'Not many. Just three quarters of their number, plus three quarters of a kitten.'

How many is that?

Puzzle 18

A ball is dropped from a height of 6 feet. It bounces up half of the original height and then falls to the ground. It repeats this, always bouncing back half the height of the previous bounce. How far does it travel?

Puzzle 19

Sophie was born in December. The sum of all the dates of the day following her birthday in the month is three times the sum of the dates of the days before her birthday in the month. What date is her birthday?

Turn to page 47 for the answers ✓

GENIUS LEVEL FOUR ANSWERS

1.
48 (They are are all perfect squares multiplied by 3, starting with 8 eg $8^2 \times 3 = 192$).

2.
90.525.

3.
736.26 units.

4.
481 (Square the numbers in the two adjacent circles and place their sum in the opposite triangle).

5.
2534.

6. 52. (All the others can be divided by 3 and 13).

7.

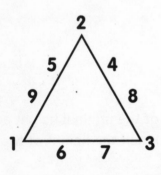

or

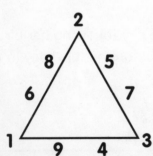

8.
Twice as large. Call half the smaller number m. The smaller number minus m is m. The larger number minus m is three times as large, or 3m. Then the smaller number is m + m = 2m and the larger number is 3m + m = 4m.

9.
There have to be two corners with a chair in so that each of the pair counts for two walls.

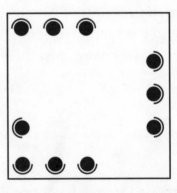

or

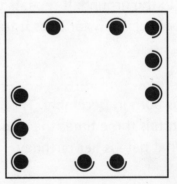

10.

58.

11.

504.

12.

15 (It will meet 13 ships at sea, and one in each harbour).

13.

7, 10, and 16.

14.

The circle is divided as shown below:

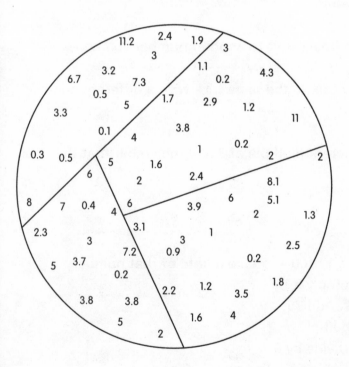

15.

1 + 1 + 2 + 4 = 1 x 1 x 2 x 4.

16.

All the amounts for each item are divisible by four (2 x 2, 5 x 4, 8 x A and 12 x B), so their total would also have to be divisible by four, but $1.70 isn't.

17.

3 (Three quarters of a kitten must equal one quarter of the total, from there it's easy).

18.

18 feet.

19.

16 December.

HINTS AND TIPS

THINK OF A NUMBER

Try this with a friend. They'll think you are a real maths wizard:

1. Think of a number between 1 and 100 and take a note of that number

2. Multiply it by 3

3. Add 45

4. Multiply by 2

5. Divide by 6

6. Subtract your original number

7. The answer is 15!

This trick works no matter what number you friend picks because you trick them into subtracting their number from the final result.

What you are really doing is changing the final result to another number you know.

If your friend wants to test you again, you can do the same trick with a different number at the end.

Just change the number in step 3 to a different multiple of 3 and remember that the final answer will be that number divided by 3.

Example:

1. Think of a number between 1 and 100 and take a note of that number

2. Multiply it by 3

3. Add 75

4. Multiply by 2

5. Divide by 6

6. Subtract your original number

7. The answer is 25!

Or if you want to be very clever, you can choose a number for step 3 that doesn't divide evenly by 3. But this time, for the final answer you'll have to memorise whatever fraction you get as a result.

Example:

1. Think of a number between 1 and 100 and take a note of that number
2. Multiply it by 3
3. Add 100
4. Multiply by 2
5. Divide by 6
6. Subtract your original number
7. The answer is 33.333333333333333333333 repeating for ever!

An alternative method is to leave off step 6 and ask your friend to tell you the result. You simply subtract your final answer from theirs and tell them the number they picked.

Example:

1. Think of a number between 1 and 100 and take a note of that number (Subject picks 8)
2. Multiply it by 3 (3 x 8 = 24)
3. Add 99   (24 + 99 = 123)
4. Multiply by 2   (123 x 2 = 246)
5. Divide by 6   (246 / 6 = 41)
6. What number do you have? (Subject says 41)
7. Subtract 33 from 41 and tell subject the original number was 8

Note: We are using 33 because we used 99 in step 3

How Think of a Number tricks work

The real secret of the trick is subtracting their original number from the result. Step 2 x step 4 of the trick always equal step 5. If you take any number and multiply it by 3 and then by 2, and then divide the result by 6, you are left with the original number. The other steps are just to confuse the subjects so they won't realise what you have done.

You can change steps 2, 4 & 5 to be whatever you want. The final answer is always step 3 divided by step 2.

Example:

1. Think of a number between 1 and 100 and take a note of that number
2. Multiply it by 16
3. Add 66
4. Multiply by 8
5. Divide by 128   (because 16 x 8 = 128)
6. Subtract your original number
7. The answer is 4.125 (66 / 16)

Now your turn:

Think of your own variation by changing the numbers for the addition and multiplication steps 2, 3, 4, 5 and the result, 7. . .

1. Think of a number between 1 and 100 and take a note of that number
2. Multiply it by _____
3. Add _____
4. Multiply by _____
5. Divide by _____
6. Subtract your original number
7. The answer is _____

FIND A PERSON'S AGE

Requirements:

Calculator

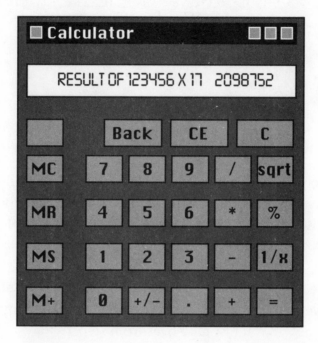

What to do

Ask a friend whose age you don't know to do the following:

1. Enter their age into a calculator
2. Multiply by 5
3. Add 5
4. Multiply by 2
5. Add 5
6. Multiply by 10
7. Give you the calculator

You then subtract 150 from the total and ignore the last two zeroes.
The result is the person's age.

Example:

1. Age: 15
2. 15 x 5 = 75
3. 75 + 5 = 80
4. 80 x 2 = 160
5. 160 + 5 = 165
6. 165 x 10 = 1650
7. (You do this) 1650 - 150 = 1500

Result: 1500 = 15

You can use this trick to work out anybody's age. It's especially useful for working out the age of teachers, parents and grandparents who don't want to give their ages. But watch out. They may be mad when they realise that you have tricked them!

Here's another example, working out a grandparent's age. Remember, your grandparent is entering everything into the calculator, following your instructions.
You just take over from step 7.

1. Age: 67
2. 67 x 5 = 335
3. 335 + 5 = 340
4. 340 x 2 = 680
5. 680 + 5 = 685
6. 685 x 10 = 6850
7. (You do this) 6850 - 150 = 6700

Result: 6700 = 67

Now try it out on some people.

DISTANCE, SPEED & TIME

As mentioned elsewhere in this book, the simple formula, distance = speed x time can be used to find any one of the variables in the equation if the other two are known.

By putting the formula into a triangle we can see that

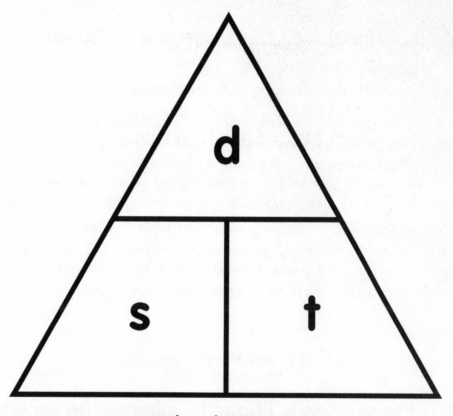

speed = distance/time

and

time = distance/speed

Let's put this to use in practical terms.

Example 1:

Q. How long will it take to travel 93 miles at 50 miles per hour?

A. Time (how long) = distance/speed = 93/50 = 1.86 hours.

Convert answer to minutes by multiplying by 60 (since there are 60 minutes in an hour).

=> 1.86 x 60 = 111.6 minutes

Since that is over an hour, subtract 60 to get the number of minutes left over 111.6 - 60 = 51.6

We also need to convert the 0.6 remainder into seconds. Do this in the same way as we converted the decimal part of the hour into minutes: multiply by 60.

=> 0.6 x 60 = 36 seconds

Thus the solution is 1 hour, 51 minutes, 36 seconds

A quick check of the answer can be done by estimation. We always know that, by definition, at 60 miles per hour we will travel 60 miles in an hour. We can double that to say that we'd travel 120 miles in two hours, at 60 miles per hour. Therefore, we can look at our solution and say that since we are travelling substantially less than 120 miles at 50 miles per hour, the answer we have arrived at is approximately right.

Example 2:

Q. If it takes Anna 5 hours to climb to Paradise at 55 steps per hour, how many steps does Anna have to climb to reach Paradise?

A. Distance (how many steps) = speed x time = 55 x 5 = 275 steps

Quick check of the answer by common sense: 55 steps per hour is almost 60. At 60 steps an hour, she'd go 300 steps in 5 hours, so our answer is approximately right. We could also do a quick check of the maths, since 5 x 50 is 250 and 5 x 5 is 25, thus 250 + 25 is 275, and we know we have the calculation right.

Example 3:

Q. How fast does a spacecraft have to travel to get from planet Aleph to the planet Delta, a distance of 320 parsecs, within 8 hours?

A. Speed (how fast) = distance/time = 320 / 8 = 40 parsecs per hour

Now answer the following questions:

a) How fast do you have to be blown in a hot air balloon to travel 150 miles in two hours?

b) It takes a snail three days to slither around a garden at 40 fence posts per day. How many fence posts enclose the garden?

c) A rich miser with one leg can hop from his begging place to the Savoy for a caviar and champagne breakfast in two hours, hopping at 3 miles per hour. How far away is the miser's begging place from the Savoy?

d) How long does it take Jasper the cat to patrol his patch of the Bronx if he travels an overall distance of 42 blocks, at an average speed of 14 blocks per hour?

e) A motorbike travels at 20 miles per hour for 1 hour, 40 miles per hour for 2 hours, and 60 miles per hour for 3 hours. What is the total distance covered by the bike?

 Turn to page 74 for the answers

SHORTCUTS

Even when using a calculator, being aware of certain patterns in the way that numbers work will help to save you a lot of time, especially if you need to use trial and error. With an instinct for what will work and what will not, you will make less mistakes and go directly to the solution more often.

1.

Any even number can be divided by 2, and possibly by multiples of 2, such as 4, 6 or 8. If you divide by 2 and the last digit of the result is even then you can divide by 2 again.

Also look for other divisors depending on the last digit. If, for example it is a 1, 2, 3, 4, 8, or 9 there is a chance that the number could be divided evenly by a 7, because 7 x 2 = 14, 7 x 4 = 28, 7 x 3 = 21 and 7 x 7 = 49.

If the last digit is a 9, you may be also able to divide it exactly by 3.

2.

Any number can be divided by 10, either by removing a 0, or by putting in or moving a decimal point. Thus, 102 / 10 = 10.2; or 1234 / 10 = 123.4; or 654670 / 10 = 65467; or 12.45/10 = 1.254. You can multiply by 10 by doing the opposite.

3.

If you multiply two figures that end in 5, the result will always end in 5.

4.

Break figures (whose tables you have not yet memorised) down to do the calculation mentally.

Therefore 15 x 15 is the same as 10 x 15 plus 5 x 15. Since 10 x 15 is 150, you can instantly divide that by 2 to get the 75 which you have to add to 150 to get the result 225.

5.

Balance multiplications. 24 X 3 is the same as 12 x 6 which is 72.
Sometimes it is easier to work out a sum by doubling the higher figure:

$$17 \times 4 = 34 \times 2 = 68$$

6.

It is often easier to break exponential powers into component powers. You can remember
or work out mentally that $2^5 = 32$ (from 2x2x2x2x2).

Therefore, it is simpler to calculate 2^{10} by working out $= (2^5)^2 = 32^2 = 1024$.
Similarly 3^4 is the same as $(3^2)^2 = (9)^2 = 81$, and 6^6 is the same as $(6^3)^2$ or $216^2 = 46656$.

7.

To multiply a number by 25, just divide by 4 and add two zeros

$$16 \times 25 = 16 / 4 = 4 + (00) = 400.$$

8.

To add 10% to something just multiply by 1.1. Similarly, to add 17.5% to something, just
multiply by 1.175, and so on. Alternatively, to find 17.5% of (say) 320, use the
following method:

10% of 320 is 32, so 5% is 16, and $2^1/2$% is 8. Simply add 32, 16, and 8 to get 56.

9.

Any even number that can be divided by 3 can also be divided by 6.

FIBONACCI NUMBERS

Around eight hundred years ago, in 1202, the mathematician Leonardo of Pisa, also called Fibonacci, published his famous treatise, Liber Abaci (it's not known if he played the piano!).

It contained the following puzzle:

"How many pairs of rabbits can be produced from a single pair in one year if it is assumed that every month each pair begets a new pair which from the second month becomes productive?"

Calculation reveals the following series:

Month	1	2	3	4	5	6	7	8	9	10	11	12
Rabbits	1	1	2	3	5	8	13	21	34	55	89	144

The second row represents the first 12 numbers of the sequence now known as Fibonacci numbers, in which each term (except the first two) is found by adding the two terms immediately in front. 1 + 1 = 2; 1 + 2 = 3; 2 + 3 = 5. . .etc.

Fibonacci numbers don't have to start from 1. Here's another series starting from 3:

3	3	6	9	15	24	39	63	102	165	267	432

Now your turn. Fill in the blanks in the following Fibonacci series:

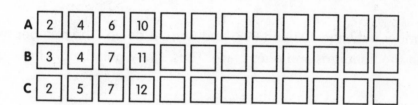

A | 2 | 4 | 6 | 10 | | | | | | | |

B | 3 | 4 | 7 | 11 | | | | | | | |

C | 2 | 5 | 7 | 12 | | | | | | | |

Now create a new Fibonacci series of your own, starting from the beginning:

✔ *Turn to page 74 for the answers*

THE 1089 TRICK

A calculation trick with different
numbers but the same 1089 answer.

Requirements:

Pencil and paper.
Calculator.
A friend to trick.

What to do:

Write the number 1089 on a piece of paper, being careful so that when the paper is upside down the number looks like 6801. Write it like the digits on a calculator, 1089.

Give your friend a pencil and a sheet of paper and tell your friend to do the following:

1. Think of a number between 102 and 998, and write it down. The number must have different digits in the hundreds and ones place. Thus, 112 would be ok, but not (say) 818.

2. Reverse the number so that 347 would become 743.

3. Subtract the larger number from the smaller number.

4. If the result is less than 100, put zeros in front until you have a three digit number. Therefore, if the answer is 38, use 038.

5. Reverse the answer from step 4 and add the result to the answer from step 4.

6. Say the answer (it will always be 1089).

Just before your friend says the answer, interrupt and say, "Don't tell me, I know it already!" and hold your bit of paper upside down so that it reads 6801. Your friend will think you have failed to predict the result, but after a pause you can surprise the friend by turning your paper up the right way and showing the correct answer.

HIDDEN NUMBERS TRICK

This one is very simple, and few people will catch on if you only do it once with each person.

Ask a friend to think of a number between 1 and 10.
Whatever they choose, you can then say, "I knew you were going to pick that number."
The friend is unlikely to believe you, so you can then say, "Go and look under the clock," (or whatever).

The secret is to write out the numbers from 1 to 10 on separate scraps of paper and hide them in places where you will remember them.

Whatever number your friend chooses, you can then recall the place where you have that number hidden and direct the friend to go and recover that scrap of paper. Unless the friend is very smart he or she will not realise that you have nine other scraps of paper hidden with the rest of the possible choices on them.

Good hiding places are memorable hiding places. Here are some that can be easily remembered because the places rhyme with the numbers or with places that can be connected with the things that rhyme with the numbers.

(1)   Under a bun (or a loaf of bread)
(2)   Inside a shoe (or a sock)
(3)   Under a tree (pot plant)
(4)   On the floor (under a rug)
(5)   On the drive (or in a car or toy car)
(6)   Under a brick (or under a terracotta ornament)
(7)   Near heaven (up high)
(8)   In the grate (on top, under, or near the fireplace)
(9)   On the line (pegged to a washing line, perhaps)
(10)   In a pen (Inside a ball point pen, wrapped around the ink refill)

THE KÖNIGSBERG BRIDGE PROBLEM

This is an ancient unsolved problem posed by the famous Swiss mathematician Euler, based on the seven bridges of the Prussian city of Königsberg (now Kaliningrad, Russia).

Here is the problem: Is it possible to cross each of the bridges just once and return to a starting point? Euler claimed the journey was not possible, and nobody has ever found a solution. If you can find a working route, you will be a real maths wizard.

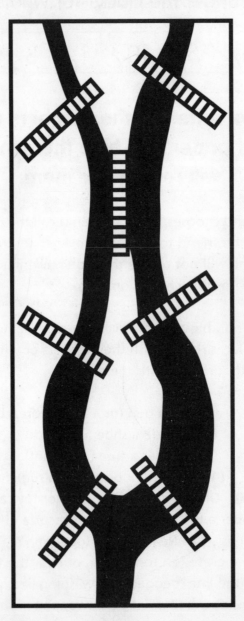

NUMBER SEQUENCES

A number sequence can be made from any group of numbers which have some kind of order that can be discovered. The simplest sequence is 1, 2, 3, 4, 5 . . . . If you were asked to predict what comes next, you'd have no difficulty in saying '6'. Similarly, with the sequence 2, 4, 6, 8, 10. . ., you are likely to realise that the next number in the sequence will be 12.

From this point, things become progressively more complicated, and it can take a practised eye to see the patterns involved. Numbers can be added together, as in the Fibonacci series, 1, 1, 2, 3, 5. . . where each number is the sum of the two numbers in front or a variation of this. They can be multiplied together, as in the increment series, 2, 3, 6, 18, 108 . . . where each number is the result of multiplying the two numbers in front. Alternatively they can each have the same quantity added, such as 2, 15, 28, 41, 54 . . . and the next number would add a further 13, to give us 67.

You may come across a reduction series such as,   . . . 48, 36, 23, 9.   What comes before 48? Answer: 59 (Each progression reduces the series by an additional 1. From 59 to 48, we lose 11; from 48 to 36 we lose 12; from 36 to 23 we lose 13; from 23 to 9 we lose 14. If there were another number in the series it would be 15 less than 9 which would give us the negative number, -6).

Since numbers are infinite, possible number sequences can be infinitely varied, and it would be impossible to go through all the variations here. You have to look for the patterns, and try out likely alternatives until you find the solution.

Here is one that looks complicated, but can be solved mentally. Insert the missing value.

1130, 1135, (_____), 1156, 1169

Answer: 1145. Sequence is found by adding the total of the digits to each sum, from left to right. Looking at the number to the left of the missing value, 1 + 1 + 3 + 5 = 10, 1135 + 10 = 1145, etc.

Now try filling in the missing values in the following:

a) 768, 192, 48, 12, (___)

b) 37, (___), 21, 13, 5

c) 5, 15, 24, (___), 39

d) (___), 26, 14, 8, 5

From this point they start to get really tough and you'll have to use the function keys of a scientific calculator to solve them.

e) 22.36, 20, 17.32, 14.14, (___)

f) (_____), 1.845098, 1.7781513, 1.69897, 1.60206

g) 0.9876883, 0.9993908, 0.97437, 0.913545, (_____)

h) 0.33r, (___), 0.125, 0.083r, 0.058

✔ *Turn to pages 74 and 75 for the answers*

AMAZE YOUR FRIENDS

Here's how you can make it appear to your friends that you have the ability to memorise very long numbers, up to and beyond an unbelievable 660 digits – without going to the trouble of actually learning the numbers. All you need to be able to do is some fairly easy mental addition.

First of all, look at the following number and see if you can find the pattern in it.

190,998,752,796,516,730,336,954,932,572,910,112,358,314,594, 370,774,156,178,538, . . . **repeat from beginning 1909987 . . .**

Did you find the pattern? (Yes / No) If not, try again before giving up.

The secret of the long number

All you need to remeber is the number 19!
Look at the beginning of the number sequence: 190,998,752...
1+9 = 10, Drop the 1 & put down the 0

$$190$$

Now add the 9 & the 0 => $9+0 = 9$

Put down the 9 => $190,9$

Now add the 0 & the 9 => $0+9 = 9$

Put down the 9 => $190,99...$

Now add the 9 & the 9 => $9+9 = 18$

Drop the 1 & put down the 8 => $190,998...$

The sequence builds, easily, step by step, with nothing to be remembered, and only a simple addition step at each stage of the calculation.

190, 998, 752, 796, 516, 730, 336, 954, 932, 572, 910, 112, 358, 314, 594, 370, 774, 156, 178, 538...

65

After 60 digits the number repeats, so if you think the person you are proving your amazing memory to will not realize that the number is repeating, you could go on for as long as you wish. Here is the sequence extended to 660 digits. Use a copy of this with the above method to astonish all those people who say you'd forget your head if it wasn't screwed on. And if that doesn't impress them, use the sequence overleaf, extended to 3,300 digits. You can also make up your own sequence by starting with a different two numbers.

660 Number Sequence

190,998,752,796,516,730,336,954,932,572,910,112,358,314,594,
370,774,156,178,538,190,998,752,796,516,730,336,954,932,572,
910,112,358,314,594,370,774,156,178,538,190,998,752,796,516,
730,336,954,932,572,910,112,358,314,594,370,774,156,178,538,
190,998,752,796,516,730,336,954,932,572,910,112,358,314,594,
370,774,156,178,538,190,998,752,796,516,730,336,954,932,572,
910,112,358,314,594,370,774,156,178,538,190,998,752,796,516,
730,336,954,932,572,910,112,358,314,594,370,774,156,178,538,
190,998,752,796,516,730,336,954,932,572,910,112,358,314,594,
370,774,156,178,538,190,998,752,796,516,730,336,954,932,572,
910,112,358,314,594,370,774,156,178,538,190,998,752,796,516,
730,336,954,932,572,910,112,358,314,594,370,774,156,178,538,
190,998,752,796,516,730,336,954,932,572,910,112,358,314,594,
370,774,156,178,538,190,998,752,796,516,730,336,954,932,572,
910,112,358,314,594,370,774,156,178,538.

3300 Number Sequence

190,998,752,796,516,730,336,954,932,572,910,112,358,314,594,370,774,156,178,
538,190,998,752,796,516,730,336,954,932,572,910,112,358,314,594,370,774,
156,178,538,190,998,752,796,516,730,336,954,932,572,910,112,358,314,594,370,
774,156,178,538,190,998,752,796,516,730,336,954,932,572,910,112,358,314,594,
370,774,156,178,538,190,998,752,796,516,730,336,954,932,572,910,112,358,314,
594,370,774,156,178,538,190,998,752,796,516,730,336,954,932,572,910,112,
358,314,594,370,774,156,178,538,190,998,752,796,516,730,336,954,932,572,
910,112,358,314,594,370,774,156,178,538,190,998,752,796,516,730,336,954,932,
572,910,112,358,314,594,370,774,156,178,538,190,998,752,796,516,730,336,954,
932,572,910,112,358,314,594,370,774,156,178,538,190,998,752,796,516,730,336,
954,932,572,910,112,358,314,594,370,774,156,178,538,190,998,752,796,516,730,
336,954,932,572,910,112,358,314,594,370,774,156,178,538,190,998,752,796,516,
730,336,954,932,572,910,112,358,314,594,370,774,156,178,538,190,998,752,
796,516,730,336,954,932,572,910,112,358,314,594,370,774,156,178,538,190,998,
752,796,516,730,336,954,932,572,910,112,358,314,594,370,774,156,178,538,190,
998,752,796,516,730,336,954,932,572,910,112,358,314,594,370,774,156,178,
538,190,998,752,796,516,730,336,954,932,572,910,112,358,314,594,370,774,
156,178,538,190,998,752,796,516,730,336,954,932,572,910,112,358,314,594,370,
774,156,178,538,190,998,752,796,516,730,336,954,932,572,910,112,358,314,594,
370,774,156,178,538,190,998,752,796,516,730,336,954,932,572,910,112,358,314,
594,370,774,156,178,538,190,998,752,796,516,730,336,954,932,572,910,112,
358,314,594,370,774,156,178,538,190,998,752,796,516,730,336,954,932,572,
910,112,358,314,594,370,774,156,178,538,190,998,752,796,516,730,336,954,932,
572,910,112,358,314,594,370,774,156,178,538,190,998,752,796,516,730,336,954,
932,572,910,112,358,314,594,370,774,156,178,538,190,998,752,796,516,730,336,
954,932,572,910,112,358,314,594,370,774,156,178,538,190,998,752,796,516,730,
336,954,932,572,910,112,358,314,594,370,774,156,178,538,190,998,752,796,516,
730,336,954,932,572,910,112,358,314,594,370,774,156,178,538,190,998,752,
796,516,730,336,954,932,572,910,112,358,314,594,370,774,156,178,538,190,998,
752,796,516,730,336,954,932,572,910,112,358,314,594,370,774,156,178,538,190,
998,752,796,516,730,336,954,932,572,910,112,358,314,594,370,774,156,178,
538,190,998,752,796,516,730,336,954,932,572,910,112,358,314,594,370,774,1
56,178,538,190,998,752,796,516,730,336,954,932,572,910,112,358,314,594,370,
774,156,178,538,190,998,752,796,516,730,336,954,932,572,910,112,358,314,594,
370,774,156,178,538,190,998,752,796,516,730,336,954,932,572,910,112,358,314,
594,370,774,156,178,538,190,998,752,796,516,730,336,954,932,572,910,112,
358,314,594,370,774,156,178,538,190,998,752,796,516,730,336,954,932,572,
910,112,358,314,594,370,774,156,178,538,190,998,752,796,516,730,336,954,932,
572,910,112,358,314,594,370,774,156,178,538,190,998,752,796,516,730,336,954,
932,572,910,112,358,314,594,370,774,156,178,538,190,998,752,796,516,730,336,
954,932,572,910,112,358,314,594,370,774,156,178,538,190,998,752,796,516,730,
336,954,932,572,910,112,358,314,594,370,774,156,178,538,190,998,752,796,516,
730,336,954,932,572,910,112,358,314,594,370,774,156,178,538,190,998,752,
796,516,730,336,954,932,572,910,112,358,314,594,370,774,156,178,538,190,998,
752,796,516,730,336,954,932,572,910,112,358,314,594,370,774,156,178,538,190,
998,752,796,516,730,336,954,932,572,910,112,358,314,594,370,774,156,178,
538,190,998,752,796,516,730,336,954,932,572,910,112,358,314,594,370,774,
156,178,538,190,998,752,796,516,730,336,954,932,572,910,112,358,314,594,370,
774,156,178,538,190,998,752,796,516,730,336,954,932,572,910,112,358,314,594,
370,774,156,178,538,190,998,752,796,516,730,336,954,932,572,910,112,358,314,
594,370,774,156,178,538,190,998,752,796,516,730,336,954,932,572,910,112,
358,314,594,370,774,156,178,538,190,998,752,796,516,730,336,954,932,572,
910,112,358,314,594,370,774,156,178,538,190,998,752,796,516,730,336,954,932,
572,910,112,358,314,594,370,774,156,178,538,190,998,752,796,516,730,336,954,
932,572,910,112,358,314,594,370,774,156,178,538,190,998,752,796,516,730,336,
954,932,572,910,112,358,314,594,370,774,156,178,538,190,998,752,796,516,730,
336,954,932,572,910,112,358,314,594,370,774,156,178,538,190,998,752,796,516,
730,336,954,932,572,910,112,358,314,594,370,774,156,178,538,190,998,752,
796,516,730,336,954,932,572,910,112,358,314,594,370,774,156,178,538.

UNKNOWN VALUES

Level 3

Algebra, the branch of mathematics that uses symbols to explore relationships between numbers, can be used to find unknown values when we have enough information to use as clues.

Example:

Animals are weighed on the following scales. Find the value of each spider, mosquito and bee.

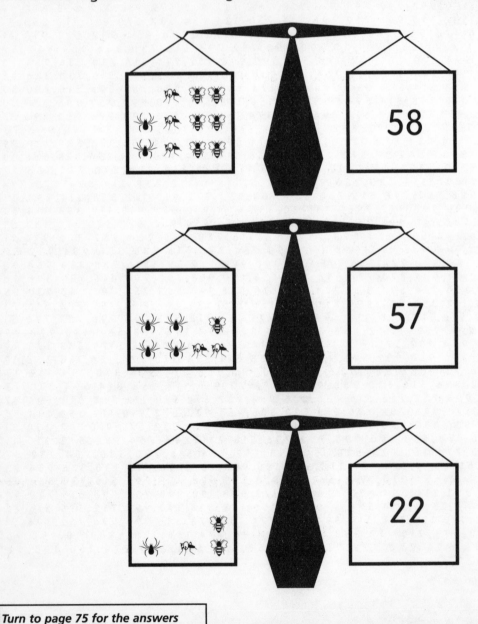

✔ **Turn to page 75 for the answers**

If you can't do this, follow the instructions overleaf
to solve this problem.
Using algebra, we will assign x for spiders, y for mosquitoes,
and z for bees.
Thus, x means 1 spider; 2x means 2 spiders; 6z
means 6 bees, etc.

The unknown weights problem can be solved as a simultaneous equation. For each line of the equation -- (each set of scales) we assign a letter that refers to that line. The first line is (a) the second is (b) and the third is (c).

Thus:

(a) $2x + 3y + 6z = 58$
(Two spiders plus three mosquitoes plus 6 bees = 58)
(b) $4x + 2y + z = 57$
(c) $x + y + 2z = 22$

Add (b) & (c) to get (d)

=> (d) $5x + 3y + 3z = 79$

(We do this so that we have 3y in another line, and can use that.)

Now eliminate y

$$=> \quad \text{(d)} \; 5x + 3y + 3z = 79$$
$$\text{subtract (a)} \; 2x + 3y + 6z = 58$$

$$3x \qquad - 3z = 21$$

Note that 3x - 3z = 21 can be divided by 3, so we'll do that to simplify, and call the answer (e)

=> (e) $x - z = 7$

Now we eliminate x & y from the equation to find z.

$$=> \quad (c) \; x + y + 2z = 22$$
$$\text{subtract} \; (e) \; x \quad\quad - z = 7$$

$$\text{Thus} \; (f) \quad y + 3z = 15$$

(Note: 2z - (-z) = 2z + z = 3z.)

$$=> (a) \times 2 => 4x + 6y + 12z = 116$$
$$\text{subtract} \; (b) \; 4x + 2y + z = 57$$

$$\text{Thus} \quad\quad 4y + 11z = 59$$

$$=> (f) \times 4 => \quad\quad 4y + 12z = 60$$
$$\text{subtract} \; (g) \quad\quad 4y + 11z = 59$$

$$z = 1$$

Now that we know z = 1, we can substitute back into (e).

$$=> (e) \; x - z = 7$$
$$\text{Thus} \quad x - 1 = 7$$
$$x = 8$$

We now know that know z = 1, and x = 8, and we can substitute back into (c).

$$(c) \quad x + y + 2z = 22$$
$$=> \quad 8 + y + 2 = 22$$
$$=> \quad\quad y = 22 - 10$$
$$=> \quad y = 12$$

Thus the problem is solved, since we know
that x (spiders) = 8; y (mosquitoes) = 12; z (bees) = 1.

Now that you know the principles involved, here is one that you should be able to do by hand.

Vehicles are weighed on the following scales. Find the value of each car, horse, and bicycle.

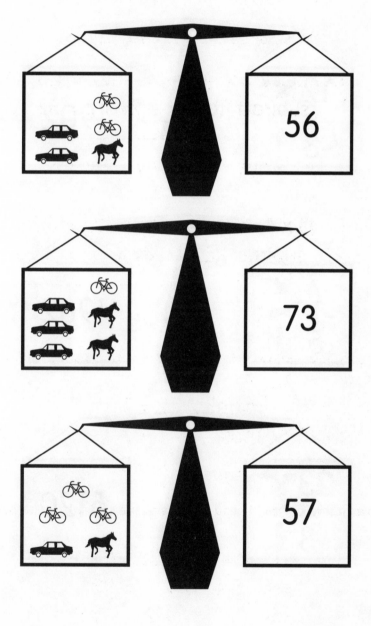

Turn to page 75 for the answers ✔

Use the calculator to help you with this one if necessary.

Eagles, rabbits, and penguins are weighed on the following scales. Find the value of each creature. In the first example here, we have 12 eagles, plus 9 rabbits, minus 3 penguins, equals 1902.

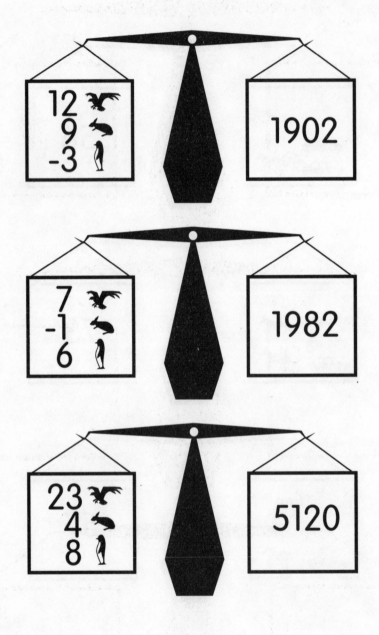

✔ *Turn to page 75 for the answers*

This is a genius level puzzle, for those with a lot of patience, who like to be really challenged. Beware, though! This puzzle looks like the others but works quite differently. Can you work out which number should replace the question mark?

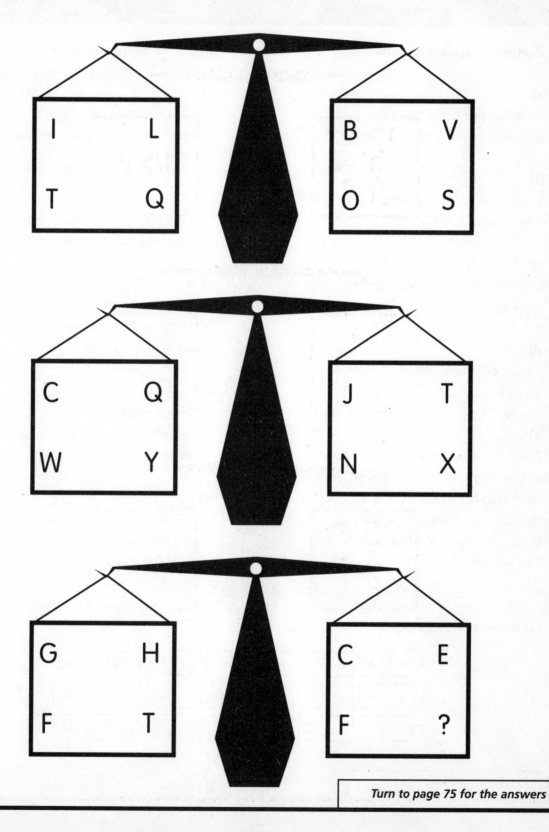

Turn to page 75 for the answers ✔

ANSWERS TO HINTS AND TIPS

Distance, Speed & Time:

a)
75 miles per hour (speed = distance / time = 150 / 2 = 75).

b)
120 fence posts distance = speed x time = 40 x 3 = 120).

c)
6 miles (distance = speed x time = 3 x 2 = 6).

d)
3 hours (time = distance / speed = 42 / 14 = 3).

e)
280 miles (distance = speed x time: in the first hour = 20 x 1 = 20, in the next two hours = 40 x 2 = 80, in the final three hours = 60 x 3 = 180, total distance therefore = 20 + 80 + 180 = 280).

Number Sequences:

a)
3 (Divide each number in the sequence by 4, to get the number to the right).

b)
29 (Subtract 8 from each number to get the number to the right).

c)
32 (Add 10 to the left hand number, 9 to the next, 8 to the next, 7 to the next).

d)
5 (Divide each number by 2, and add 1, to get the next number to the right).

e)
10 (The numbers are, from left to right, the square roots of 500, 400, 300, 200, 100).

Fibonacci Numbers:

A	2	4	6	10	16	26	42	68	110	178	288	466
B	3	4	7	11	18	29	47	76	123	199	322	521
C	2	5	7	12	19	31	50	81	131	212	343	555

f)

1.90309 (From left to right the numbers are the Logarithms of 80, 70, 60, 50, 40).

g)

0.819152 (From left to right, the numbers are the sines of 99, 88, 77, 66, and 55).

h)

0.2 (From left to right the numbers are the decimal equivalents of 1/3, 1/5, 1/8, 1/12, 1/17; denominators are increasing by an amount that increases by 1 each time: 3 + 2 = 5; + 3 = 8; + 4 = 12; + 5 = 17).

Unknown Values:

a)

Cars = 9; Bicycles = 10; Horses = 18

b)

Eagles = 168; Rabbits = 34; Penguins = 140

c)

X. The letters represent numbers based on their position in the alphabet, and not simultaneous equations at all. Z = 1, and A = 26. Therefore , G + H + F + T = 70.

GAMES

NUMEROLOGY

Here is a method of telling your fun fortune (or anybody else's) using just a calculator.

Have you ever noticed how certain numbers keep cropping up in your life? Perhaps you have always lived in a house numbered 1, and were born on the first day of the first month of the year? Perhaps your phone number is the same as your birthday? Perhaps you have noticed that good things happen to you on dates that have a 7 in them?

Number 13, for example, is thought to be unlucky for some, but lucky for others. Traditional methods of fortune telling depend on a random element such as shuffling a pack of tarot cards, combined with personal input from the person who is to have the reading. There also needs to be a personal contribution from the person doing the reading. Certain cards hold certain meanings, but intuition and experience must be used in the interpretation.

The following method of prediction is loosely based on Cabalistic meanings for numbers, and uses the tarot principle of introducing a random element and personal input, in this case with the calculator. When you ask them to choose, the choice they make is linked up with their fate, or so the legends say. If their fate was to be different from the one predicted, they'd have chosen a different number.

This is for fun only, so don't take it at all seriously.

Now ⟶ The Future
2 0 9 8 7 5 2

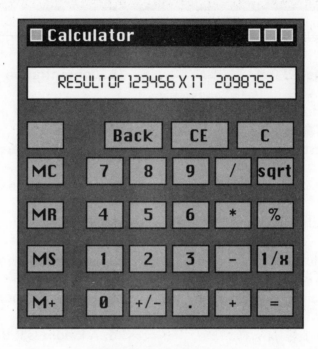

How it Works

To read someone's fortune, first enter 123456 into the calculator.

Ask the subject whose fortune is being read, to say any number between 1 and 20.

Multiply the 123456 in the calculator by the number the subject gives you.

The resulting total is the basis of your prediction.

Reading from left to right goes from the present into the future.

Start with the left hand number and note down the meanings from the chart overleaf. Do not make your interpretation until you have noted all the meanings and can see a trend in the way the meanings are operating and can tie it in with what you already know.

Never give a bad reading – it's all in fun. The golden rule is to leave people feeling good. Numbers have significance on their own as well as in combination with others, according to the overleaf table of numbers and combinations, and their Cabalistic meanings.

CABALISTIC MEANING OF NUMBERS

1. Work takes priority.

2. Satisfaction achieved.

3. Success in a venture.

4. Hope for the best.

5. Luck is on your side.

6. Your dearest wishes attained.

7. Fight against injustice.

8. Help others, and you help yourself.

9. Helpful friends.

10. Guard against loss of friends or property.

11. Let go of the old and welcome the new.

12. Expect promotion or advancement.

13. Real happiness.

14. Love grows between you and another.

15. Wealth and power possible.

16. Wedding bells ring.

17. Beware of arguments and fights.

18. Concentration on pleasure.

19. A windfall of money or property.

20. Beware of liars.

21. Someone is jealous.

22. A gift arrives.

23. Love takes priority.

24. Fame calls your name.

25. A kindness is done for you.

26. Success follows hard work.

27. A period of great change.

28. The end of a struggle.

29. Reward for efforts.

30. Trouble caused by a cheat.

31. Deep and lasting happiness.

32. Sudden fortune.

33. A time for rest and peace.

34. Assistance by a friend.

35. Ambition pays off.

36. Health matters take priority.

Additional combinations and notes

1111	Love troubled.
101010	An important matter settled.
1010	Unexpected good luck.
999	Happiness, health and wealth.
88	A love affair.
910	Birth of a child.
79	Trouble for the unwary.

1. Get the atmosphere right. Make it as inspiring as possible. Cover the calculator with a velvet cloth and don't let the subject see what you are doing.

2. Work out your fun predictions based on the Cabalistic meanings.

3. Don't go against common sense. Use what you know about the subject in your reading.

4. Before you make the reading, ask the subject if there is anything they want to find out. You will then have that in mind when you are making your interpretation, and it will help to inspire you.

5. Don't overcommit yourself, and remind people it's not serious. Choose your words carefully and nobody will be able to come back to you and say, "That didn't happen."

If, for example, wedding bells are indicated, don't predict the marriage of your subject. Just say that there will be wedding bells. You have no way of knowing what the context of those bells will be. Similarly, fame could mean that the subject is meeting a famous person. It doesn't always mean that the subject will become famous.

6. Start with what is happening now, and work your way through the numbers into the future.

Sample reading

Sample numerology reading based on a subject choosing 20

Example:

$$123456 \times 20 = 2\ 4\ 6\ 9\ 1\ 2\ 0$$

2 Right now should prove to be a great time for you, with a lot of satisfaction.

4 You are hoping for something to happen. The Cabala indicates that it may happen very soon.

6 This reinforces what I have just said. If you really believe in yourself and do what needs to be done, your dearest wishes can come true.

9 Whatever you are doing, it may be worth asking for the help of your friends. That's what they are there for.

1 The time is not far away when you will need to buckle down and do things that you have been putting off. The effort will be worthwhile.

2 The future looks very good for you. This is another indication that your long term goals can be achieved.

Ignore the zero at the end. Now look at the double number combinations.

24 Fame is calling out your name. If that is what you want, there is a chance that you could achieve it. Or perhaps you could be meeting someone famous.

12 Things are likely to go well at school (or work). You could be going on to a more advanced course (or getting promoted).

20 Looking at the future, beware of putting your trust in deceivers.

The simple outline prophecies are converted into a reading that gives positive advice and can never make someone feel bad. Whatever fortune awaits us it is always better to make the best of circumstances as they occur.

Personal Lucky Numbers

There is a traditional way of working out your lucky numbers based on your name, place of birth, and birthday. Most people have about six numbers that are lucky for them. Here is how to find them.

Lucky Numbers Associated with your Name

Mark down the values for each letter of your name into the alphanumeric grid and add up the total value.

Example:

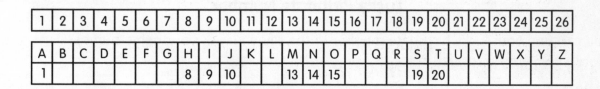

1	2	3	4	5	6	7	8	9	10	11	12	13	14	15	16	17	18	19	20	21	22	23	24	25	26
A	B	C	D	E	F	G	H	I	J	K	L	M	N	O	P	Q	R	S	T	U	V	W	X	Y	Z
1							8	9	10			13	14	15			19	20							

NAME: Joan Smith

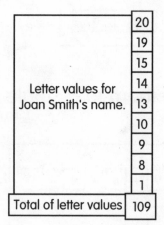

Letter values for Joan Smith's name.	20
	19
	15
	14
	13
	10
	9
	8
	1
Total of letter values	109

Add total of letter values together to get lucky name number:

$$1 + 0 + 9 = 10$$

10 is a double figure, so do the same again:

$$1 + 0 = 1$$

Joan Smith's lucky name number is 1 and she is likely to find that the number 1 is very important in her life. If she is choosing a raffle ticket, she'd be better with the very first one. If she is buying a house, she should buy number 1. If she is asked to choose between five options, she will often be better to take the first option.

Looking back at the Cabalistic quality associated with Joan's name number we can see that work will be very important for her. The number 10 will also be significant.

Now work out your own lucky name number. Be sure to use the name that you use most often, including any middle name or initials. If you have a nickname, work that out separately. Nicknames are less important Cabalistically.

1	2	3	4	5	6	7	8	9	10	11	12	13	14	15	16	17	18	19	20	21	22	23	24	25	26
A	B	C	D	E	F	G	H	I	J	K	L	M	N	O	P	Q	R	S	T	U	V	W	X	Y	Z

Lucky name number: _____

Lucky Birthdate Number

You can find your lucky birthdate number in the same way as your name number. First write down your birthdate.

	Day		Month		Year			
eg:	2	3	0	6	1	9	8	4
	Day		Month		Year			
Now Yours								

Now add the values and reduce them to a single figure.

eg:

2 + 3 + 0 + 6 + 1 + 9 + 8 + 4 = 33

3 + 3 = 6

Now Yours

☐ + ☐ + ☐ + ☐ + ☐ + ☐ + ☐ + ☐ = ☐

☐ + ☐ = ☐

Look back now at the Cabalistic quality associated with your lucky birthdate number.

Lucky Place of Birth Number

You can find your place of birth number in the same way as your name and birthdate numbers. First write down your place of birth and note the values for each letter of your place of birth into the alphanumeric grid and add up the total value. The number revealed will have a lot of meaning in your life.

Example:

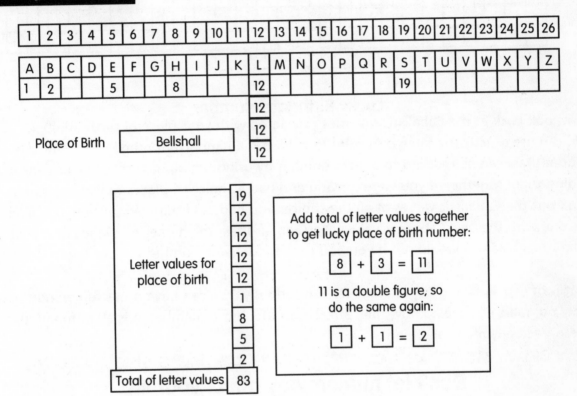

Looking back at he Cabalistic quality associated with 2 we can see that the numbers suggest a person with the place of birth number 2 will have a very satisfying life. 11 will also be an important number for somebody born in a place called Bellshall. And since the number 12 occurs 4 times, it may have importance.

Now work out your own lucky place of birth number. Find out from your parents where you were born. Don't assume that it was in the same place that you now live.

1	2	3	4	5	6	7	8	9	10	11	12	13	14	15	16	17	18	19	20	21	22	23	24	25	26
A	B	C	D	E	F	G	H	I	J	K	L	M	N	O	P	Q	R	S	T	U	V	W	X	Y	Z

Now look back at the Cabalistic qualities associated with your place of birth number. You can use exactly the same principles to work out all important numbers in your life. Your address can be reduced to a lucky number by using the alphanumeric values and adding them together. If you were moving and had a choice of places to live, you could work out the Cabalistic values of all the choices you had, and think about how you liked the one with the best Cabalistic values. You can also test the names of friends to see what Cabalistic value you would get if you add their lucky name number to your own.

That is of course taking numerology far too seriously. You can have great fun working out lucky numbers and seeing how they affect your life, but remember, it is all in fun, and doesn't actually mean anything.

Don't let numerology affect your life.

FIVE ALIVE

Requirements:

2 Players.
Pencils and paper.
Calculator.
Pair of dice.

How it Works

The object is to get as close as possible to a total of 5 without going over.

Toss a coin to decide who goes first.

Roll two dice.

Enter the result into the calculator as a decimal fraction eg, 5 + 2 = 0.52 or 0.25 (you can choose which, but not 5.2, or 2.5) then hit the + symbol.

Player 2 then repeats the process by rolling the dice again, entering the result and hitting the + symbol. Thus player 2's entered figure is added to the total already in, and the calculator is ready to pass back to player 1.

First player to go over 5 loses the game (busts). You then start over from 0.
Thus, the closer you get to 5 the tougher it is for your opponent to play without busting.

Rules:

The calculation of whether to add the lower or higher decimal combination of dice numbers must be done mentally.

It is not permitted to enter the number into the calculator and then change your mind and try again.

There are 5 games in each set.
The winner is the player who goes bust the least.
The loser goes first with the next throw of the dice.

Example game:

Player	Roll	Entered	Total
1	6 & 3	0.63	0.63
2	4& 5	0.54	1.17
1	5 & 1	0.51	1.68
2	2 & 6	0.62	2.30
1	3 & 2	0.32	2.62
2	3 & 5	0.53	3.15
1	4 & 3	0.43	3.58
2	4 & 2	0.42	4.00
1	1 & 5	0.51	4.51
2	5 & 4	0.45	4.96
1	2 & 2	0.22	5.18 BUST

Player 2 wins this game.

Five Alive Scoreboards

Draw a line under the current total and return to 0 whenever a player goes bust

Player	Roll	Entered	Total
1			
2			
1			
2			
1			
2			
1			
2			
1			
2			
1			
2			
1			
2			
1			
2			
1			
2			
1			

Player	Roll	Entered	Total
1			
2			
1			
2			
1			
2			
1			
2			
1			
2			
1			
2			
1			
2			
1			
2			
1			
2			
1			

Draw a line under the current total and return to 0 whenever a player goes bust

Player	Roll	Entered	Total	Player	Roll	Entered	Total
1				1			
2				2			
1				1			
2				2			
1				1			
2				2			
1				1			
2				2			
1				1			
2				2			
1				1			
2				2			
1				1			
2				2			
1				1			
2				2			
1				1			
2				2			
1				1			
2				2			
1				1			
2				2			
1				1			
2				2			
1				1			
2				2			
1				1			
2				2			
1				1			
2				2			
1				1			
2				2			
1				1			
2				2			
1				1			
2				2			

ESP

Requirements:

3 Players.
ESP results board.
Calculator.
Large book.

ESP stands for Extra Sensory Perception: the legendary ability to supposedly sense information about external events using a psychic awareness such as telepathy, clairvoyance, and precognition. This game pretends to use the natural psychic abilities you are supposed to have to predict numbers that a friend enters into the calculator. Of course, it's all in fun and shouldn't be taken seriously.

Precautions

Take care, when taking your turn, to enter your number in secret so that the other player has no way of seeing the position of your fingers when you hit the buttons. A good way to do this is to stand a large book open on the table between you, so that each player's hands are hidden from view of the other player.

When entering numbers, great care should be taken to keep the numbers as random as possible, otherwise you may simply reveal that you have a preference for a certain number. Many people, if asked to choose a number between 1 and 10 will choose 6 or 7, so you have to eliminate all such tendencies, to make the numbers you choose truly unpredictable.

How it works

Player 1   guesses a number between 0 and 9 inclusive, and enters it into the calculator.
Player 2   guesses aloud what that number was.
Player 1   holds up the calculator to reveal the number.
Player 3   notes down the results on the ESP results board, whether a right or wrong guess.
Player 1   then guesses another number between 0 and 9 inclusive, and enters it into the calculator.
Player 2   guesses aloud what that number was.
Player 1   holds up the calculator to reveal the number.
Player 3   notes down the results on the ESP results board, whether a right or wrong guess.

and so on . . . for 100 guesses. Then switch players.

Statistically, out of every 100 guesses, you should get around 10 correct guesses. If you score significantly better or worse, there is a chance that you may have some psychic abilities, or have been lucky. It is best to do at least 1000 guesses for each player before working out your overall score. The greater the number of tries, the less chance there is of statistical anomalies affecting your result. It is possible, purely by chance to make ten or more correct guesses in a row. This doesn't mean that you have psychic ability. The next ten guesses could all be wrong. You can only eliminate chance effects like this by using very large sampling. If a TV company were doing research to see what percentage of the population was watching a particular show, they would have to knock on more than 10 doors to have a good sample of the population on which to base their results.

Looking at larger sampling rates, the usual score to be expected is around 100 correct guesses out of every 1000 tries. (The 1 in 10 correct score indicated by chance). Much less or more than that could in theory indicate psychic ability or good luck. It has been shown in many experiments that while some people show a surprising ability to predict numbers correctly, others sometimes defy logic, not by scoring much better than chance would predict, but by scoring much worse than chance would predict. If this happens with you, you'd be better to guess what you don't think the number would be. Then you'd be more likely to get it right.

The Graph

Use the graph below to find your degree of psychic ability per 1000 guesses. If you don't have time to make a thousand guesses, you can extrapolate (predict a result) from the number you do make, but your results will have less accuracy. To extrapolate your results, divide 1000 by the number of guesses you made and multipy your amount of correct guesses by the result.

Working from 200 guesses for the chart below, since 1000 / 200 = 5, multiply the number of correct guesses out of 200 (say 39) by 5, 39 x 5 = 195. Looking at the chart below you draw a line up from the base at the position of your score until it hits the diagonal line. Then you draw a horizontal line from the diagonal to see your degree of fun psychic ability. 195 has been done for you.

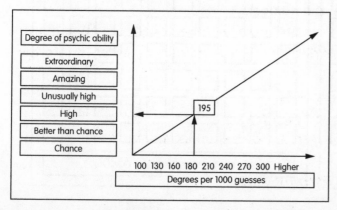

Don't extrapolate from less than 100 guesses, as the results will be meaningless.

Example:

The guessed numbers are read across. Six results boards are provided for you.

ESP Results Boards

Name:

1	2	3	4	5	6	7	8	9	10

Total correct guesses out of 100:

Name:

1	2	3	4	5	6	7	8	9	10

Total correct guesses out of 100:

Name:

	1	2	3	4	5	6	7	8	9	10
	☐	☐	☐	☐	☐	☐	☐	☐	☐	☐
	☐	☐	☐	☐	☐	☐	☐	☐	☐	☐
	☐	☐	☐	☐	☐	☐	☐	☐	☐	☐
	☐	☐	☐	☐	☐	☐	☐	☐	☐	☐
	☐	☐	☐	☐	☐	☐	☐	☐	☐	☐
	☐	☐	☐	☐	☐	☐	☐	☐	☐	☐
	☐	☐	☐	☐	☐	☐	☐	☐	☐	☐
	☐	☐	☐	☐	☐	☐	☐	☐	☐	☐
	☐	☐	☐	☐	☐	☐	☐	☐	☐	☐
	☐	☐	☐	☐	☐	☐	☐	☐	☐	☐

Total correct guesses out of 100:

Name:

	1	2	3	4	5	6	7	8	9	10
	☐	☐	☐	☐	☐	☐	☐	☐	☐	☐
	☐	☐	☐	☐	☐	☐	☐	☐	☐	☐
	☐	☐	☐	☐	☐	☐	☐	☐	☐	☐
	☐	☐	☐	☐	☐	☐	☐	☐	☐	☐
	☐	☐	☐	☐	☐	☐	☐	☐	☐	☐
	☐	☐	☐	☐	☐	☐	☐	☐	☐	☐
	☐	☐	☐	☐	☐	☐	☐	☐	☐	☐
	☐	☐	☐	☐	☐	☐	☐	☐	☐	☐
	☐	☐	☐	☐	☐	☐	☐	☐	☐	☐
	☐	☐	☐	☐	☐	☐	☐	☐	☐	☐

Total correct guesses out of 100:

Name:

	1	2	3	4	5	6	7	8	9	10
	☐	☐	☐	☐	☐	☐	☐	☐	☐	☐
	☐	☐	☐	☐	☐	☐	☐	☐	☐	☐
	☐	☐	☐	☐	☐	☐	☐	☐	☐	☐
	☐	☐	☐	☐	☐	☐	☐	☐	☐	☐
	☐	☐	☐	☐	☐	☐	☐	☐	☐	☐
	☐	☐	☐	☐	☐	☐	☐	☐	☐	☐
	☐	☐	☐	☐	☐	☐	☐	☐	☐	☐
	☐	☐	☐	☐	☐	☐	☐	☐	☐	☐
	☐	☐	☐	☐	☐	☐	☐	☐	☐	☐
	☐	☐	☐	☐	☐	☐	☐	☐	☐	☐

Total correct guesses out of 100:

Name:

	1	2	3	4	5	6	7	8	9	10
	☐	☐	☐	☐	☐	☐	☐	☐	☐	☐
	☐	☐	☐	☐	☐	☐	☐	☐	☐	☐
	☐	☐	☐	☐	☐	☐	☐	☐	☐	☐
	☐	☐	☐	☐	☐	☐	☐	☐	☐	☐
	☐	☐	☐	☐	☐	☐	☐	☐	☐	☐
	☐	☐	☐	☐	☐	☐	☐	☐	☐	☐
	☐	☐	☐	☐	☐	☐	☐	☐	☐	☐
	☐	☐	☐	☐	☐	☐	☐	☐	☐	☐
	☐	☐	☐	☐	☐	☐	☐	☐	☐	☐
	☐	☐	☐	☐	☐	☐	☐	☐	☐	☐

Total correct guesses out of 100:

MAGIC SQUARES

Magic squares are squares where each long diagonal, column, and row adds to the same value.

8	1	6
3	5	7
4	9	2

For example,
in this square each column, row and diagonal adds up to 15.

There are many different ways to do magic squares and it is easy to go wrong with just one number. The golden rule to remember is that you will never find the same number on the same row, column, or diagonal. Solutions to the following problems are at the end of this chapter.

Magic Square Problem 1

Use the same 5 numbers for the rest of the rows and put them in such a way that each row, column, and long diagonal adds to 21.
This type of magic square is known as a Latin Square.

9	6	1	3	2

✔ *Turn to page 100 for the answers*

Magic Square Problem 2

Here is another Latin square.
Use the same 5 numbers that have been used below and fill in the rest of the square in such a way that each row, column, and long diagonal adds to 20.

8				0
4				
2	8	4	0	6
0				
6				2

Magic Square Problem 3

This true magic square uses all the numbers from 1 to 25.
Fill in the blanks in such a way that each row, column, and long diagonal adds to 65.

17	24	1	8	15
23				16
4				22
10				3
11	18	25	2	9

Turn to page 100 for the answers ✔

Magic Square Problem 4

This magic square is numbered from 1 to 36.

Fill in the blanks in such a way that each row, column, and long diagonal adds to 111.

21	23	25	27	8	7
24					6
1					35
4					34
29					15
32	30	12	10	13	14

Magic Square Problem 5

This magic square is numbered from 1 to 49.

Fill in the blanks in such a way that each row, column, and long diagonal adds to 175.

20	11	2	49	40	31	22
12	3					21
4		42				13
45			25			5
37				8		46
29					47	38
28	19	10	1	48	39	30

✔ *Turn to page 100 for the answers*

Magic Square Problem 6

This magic square is numbered from 1 to 64.
Fill in the blanks in such a way that each row, column, and long diagonal adds to 260

57	16	24	33	25	48	56	1
7	50					10	63
6		43			19		62
60			36	28			4
61			37	29			5
3		46			22		59
2	55					15	58
64	9	17	40	32	41	49	8

Magic Square Problem 7

This magic square is numbered from 1 to 100, and is known as a LUX square because of the way each block of 4 is filled in either in an L, U, or X pattern. (OK, it's not a perfect analogy!) The missing numbers are provided in blocks. Don't split the blocks. Insert each block to fill in the blanks in such a way that each row, column, and long diagonal adds to 505.

34	35	6	7	98	99	70	71	42	43
36	33	8	5	100	97	72	69	44	41
11	10							39	38
12	9							40	37
87	86							15	14
85	88							13	16
63	62							91	90
61	64							89	92
59	58	31	30	3	2	95	94	67	66
57	60	29	32	1	4	93	96	65	68

Turn to page 100 for the answers

Magic Square Problem 8

Insert the missing numbers so that each row, column and long diagonal, multiply together
to produce 2,058,068,231,856,000.
The missing numbers are provided in blocks of two.
Don't split the blocks.

203	78	75	68	27	30	207	152
200		58	13	92	57		105
76		90	189	136	225		29
15							100
102							243
117		17	50	45	108		138
81		161	114	261	104		34
46	19	216	135	150	119	116	39

162		171		153		54		232
26		52		69		175		60

184		91		174		133		51
87		38		23		25		120

✔ *Turn to page 101 for the answers*

Magic Square Problem 9

All the numbers have been given in the magic square below.
All you have to do is look at the square and figure out what is so special about it.
Five blank squares are provided to allow you to experiment.

18	8	31	9	60	46	53	35
55	33	58	48	29	11	20	6
62	44	51	37	24	2	25	15
27	13	22	4	49	39	64	42
5	19	12	30	47	57	34	56
36	54	45	59	10	32	7	17
41	63	40	50	3	21	14	28
16	26	1	23	38	52	43	61

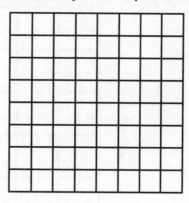

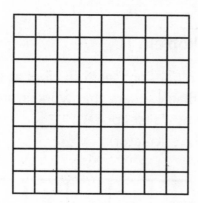

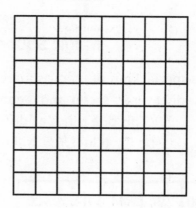

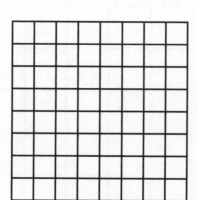

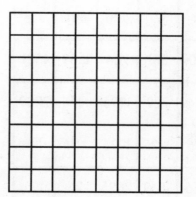

Turn to page 101 for the answers ✔

Magic Square Problem 10

Fill in the blanks of this magic square in such a way that each row, column, and long diagonal adds to 1.3

0.34	0.48	0.02	0.16	0.3
0.46				0.32
0.08				0.44
0.2				0.06
0.22	0.36	0.5	0.04	0.18

Magic Square Problem 11

This is a special kind of magic square that does not seem to work at first.
Can you discover its secret and create a magic square that works from it?
This one is not as difficult as it first appears.
(Clue: You will need a calculator)

1024	1681	2500	9	144	441	900
1600	2401	81	121	400	841	961
2304	64	100	361	784	1369	1521
49	256	324	729	1296	1444	2209
225	289	676	1225	1936	2116	36
529	625	1156	1849	2025	25	196
576	1089	1764	2601	16	169	484

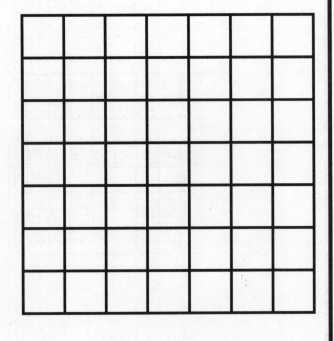

✔ **Turn to page 101 for the answers**

Magic Square Problem 12

(Genius level)

This is a another special magic square that does not seem to work at first.
You have to work with the columns to discover its secret and create a magic square that
works. Five blanks have been provided to allow you to test out some options.
(Clue: You should not need a calculator).

A	B	C	D	E	F	G
18	8	-2	44	34	24	14
10	0	39	36	26	16	13
2	41	38	28	18	8	5
43	33	30	20	10	7	-3
35	32	22	12	2	-1	38
27	24	14	4	1	40	30
26	16	6	-4	42	32	22

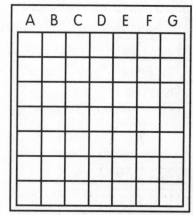

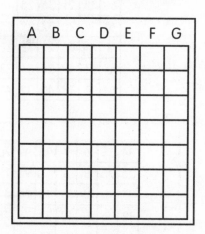

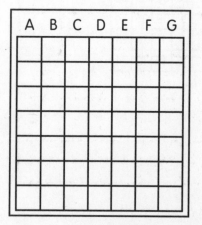

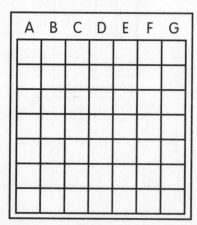

Turn to page 101 for the answers ✔

ANSWERS TO GAMES

1.

9	6	1	3	2
3	2	9	6	1
6	1	3	2	9
2	9	6	1	3
1	3	2	9	6

2.

8	2	6	4	0
4	0	8	2	6
2	6	4	0	8
0	8	2	6	4
6	4	0	8	2

3.

17	24	1	8	15
23	5	7	14	16
4	6	13	20	22
10	12	19	21	3
11	18	25	2	9

4.

21	23	25	27	8	7
24	22	28	26	5	6
1	3	20	19	33	35
4	2	17	18	36	34
29	31	9	11	16	15
32	30	12	10	13	14

5.

20	11	2	49	40	31	22
12	3	43	41	32	23	21
4	44	42	33	24	15	13
45	36	34	25	16	14	5
37	35	26	17	8	6	46
29	27	18	9	7	47	38
28	19	10	1	48	39	30

6.

57	16	24	33	25	48	56	1
7	50	42	31	39	18	10	63
6	51	43	30	38	19	11	62
60	13	21	36	28	45	53	4
61	12	20	37	29	44	52	5
3	54	46	27	35	22	14	59
2	55	47	26	34	23	15	58
64	9	17	40	32	41	49	8

7.

34	35	6	7	98	99	70	71	42	43
36	33	8	5	100	97	72	69	44	41
11	10	83	82	75	74	47	46	39	38
12	9	84	81	73	76	48	45	40	37
87	86	79	78	51	50	23	22	15	14
85	88	77	80	52	49	21	24	13	16
63	62	55	54	27	26	19	18	91	90
61	69	53	56	25	28	17	20	89	92
59	58	31	30	3	2	95	94	67	66
57	60	29	32	1	4	93	96	65	68

8.

If you were astute you may have noticed that each row, column, and long diagonal also add to 840, an easier way of finding the solution.

203	78	75	68	27	30	207	152
200	153	58	13	92	57	162	105
76	69	90	189	136	225	26	29
15	54	171	184	91	174	51	100
102	175	52	87	38	23	120	243
117	232	17	50	45	108	133	138
81	60	161	114	261	104	25	34
49	19	216	135	150	119	116	39

9.

The special feature of this magic square in which each row, column, and long diagonal adds to 260, is that squaring each of the numbers produces another magic square in which each row, column, and long diagonal adds to 11,180.

10.

0.34	0.48	0.02	0.16	0.3
0.46	0.1	0.14	0.28	0.32
0.08	0.12	0.26	0.4	0.44
0.2	0.24	0.38	0.42	0.06
0.22	0.36	0.5	0.04	0.18

11.

When the square root of each number is taken, this produces the following magic square in which each row, column, and long diagonal adds to 189.

32	41	50	3	12	21	30
40	49	9	11	20	29	31
48	8	10	19	28	37	39
7	16	18	27	36	38	47
15	17	26	35	44	46	6
23	25	34	43	45	5	14
24	33	42	51	4	13	22

12.

Working from left to right subtract 7 from each figure in column A, 6 from column B, 5 from column C, and so on down to 1 from column G. This produces the magic square below in which each row, column, and long diagonal adds to 112.

A	B	C	D	E	F	G
11	2	-7	40	31	22	13
3	-6	34	32	23	14	12
-5	35	33	24	15	6	4
36	27	25	16	7	5	-4
28	26	17	8	-1	-3	37
20	18	9	0	-2	38	29
19	10	1	-8	39	30	21

WOULD YOU BELIEVE IT ?

RANDOM NUMBERS

There are a number of games where it could be useful to have a good method of picking random numbers.

Here are five reliable methods.

1. Ping Pong Balls   (But you could use scraps of paper)

Write the numbers from 1 to (whatever) on ping pong balls and put the balls in a bag with a narrow neck. People have to pick the numbers out without looking. Here someone has chosen numbers that total 120, but they could be combined in any way you like. For example, you could add or multiply the value of the balls together.

2. Roll two dice.

By combining the results you obtain any of 36 random numbers between 2 and 66. You could choose to use the nearest die to you as the 10s and the other one as the units. Thus the roll below could be 46 or 64.

3. Cards

Cut a pack of cards with the face cards removed. Replace each selected card after recording its value and ensure the pack is well shuffled between each few cuts. The numbers you draw can be combined. Here, using 4 cards, a total of 21 has been drawn, but you could multiply the numbers instead, to get 10 x 2 x 5 x 4 = 400, or you could multiply the first two together (10 x 2 = 20), add the second two together (5 + 4 = 9) and take the highest from the lowest figure (20 - 9 = 11). The process can be varied as you like.

4. Time

Multiply a number by the time, including seconds. Computers use a variation of this method, using the system time as a starting basis for their randomisation.

Here, on this Roman numeral clock face the hour hand is at 8, the minute hand is at (say) 9, and the second hand is at (say) 2, so we could multiply 8 x 9 x 2 = 144, or we could add the numbers to get 8 + 9 + 2 = 19. You just decide first which method you will use. If you need more than one random number, unless the clock is broken you won't find the hands in the same place the next time you look (unless you look at exactly the same time of day on another day).

5. Binary Coins

Tossing coins is by nature a binary process, since there are only two possible ways a coin can land (discounting the slight possibility of the coin landing on its edge). It also has the benefit of having a random result. It is difficult to toss a coin by spinning it in the air and have it land in a way that you can predict. Thus it lends itself to the operation of choosing random numbers. Simply allocate heads as 1 and tails as 0, make a number of tosses and convert the result into a decimal number. Here 6 tosses have been made, resulting in the binary 101100, which adds to 44.

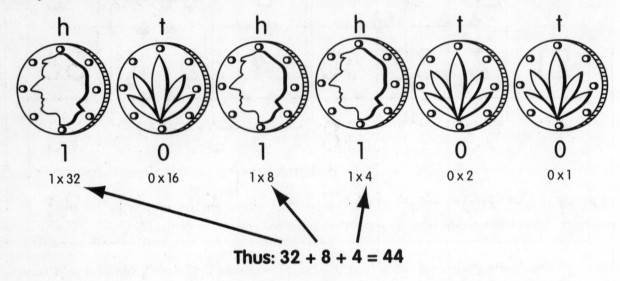

Thus: 32 + 8 + 4 = 44

6. Board

Roll a coin onto a board marked with numbers. Add up the numbers of any square the coin lands in, plus the numbers of any square whose borders the coin is in.

Example:

Here a coin has landed on the junction of 38, 10, 43, and 36. Adding these gives us 127. Or we could concatenate (link together) the 127 by adding the digits together to give us 1 + 2 + 7 = 10.

6	37	15	50	1	58	7	44
9	28	5	12	16	22	38	43
21	2	32	40	24	52	10	36
47	53	17	48	33	39	23	18
46	29	14	27	30	51	61	31
59	20	45	49	60	35	13	8
26	34	54	41	3	55	18	56
64	11	25	57	63	42	62	4

Coin Rolling Board

6	37	15	50	1	58	7	44
9	28	5	12	16	22	38	43
21	2	32	40	24	52	10	36
47	53	17	48	33	39	23	18
46	29	14	27	30	51	61	31
59	20	45	49	60	35	13	8
26	34	54	41	3	55	18	56
64	11	25	57	63	42	62	4

ASTRONOMICAL NUMBERS

Light-Year

Light moves at the amazingly fast speed of 299,792,458 metres (186,282 miles) per second, so it travels a very long way in a year: about 9.46053×10^{12} km (nine quadrillion, four hundred and sixty trillion, five hundred and thirty billion kilometres). That is the equivalent of 5.878×10^{12} miles, or 63,240 times the average distance from the earth to the sun. We call the distance from the earth to the sun one astronomical unit.

Accurate values for the length of the astronomical unit have been obtained by timing radar reflections from Venus and by measuring the distance from the surface of the Moon by bouncing laser signals off a mirror placed on the lunar surface by astronauts. The timing of the return signal is so accurate that the distance between the observatory (that transmits the signal) and the reflecting surface on the Moon can be determined to within 2.5 cm (1 inch).

But in astronomy, distances are huge, so even astronomical units are too small to measure interstellar spaces. Therefore, astronomers use the parsec, the kiloparsec (equal to 1000 parsecs) and the megaparsec equal to 1,000,000 parsecs. One parsec is equal to about 3.262 light-years. As an example of the huge distances involved, the nearest triple-star system to us, Alpha Centauri, is 1.33 parsecs away. At current spacecraft speeds of around 55,000 miles per hour, it would take us over 52,000 years to get there.

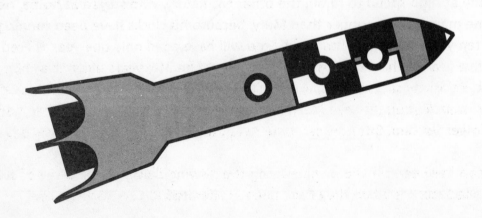

Our sun is at a distance of 8.5 kiloparsecs from the centre of the Milky Way system, the galaxy which we belong to. The distance to the Andromeda Galaxy (Messier 31) is about 0.7 megaparsec, or 700,000 parsecs. Some galaxies and quasars have likely distances of about 3,000 megaparsecs, which means that they are approximately 10,000,000,000 light-years away from us.

This also means that when we look into space we are looking into the past. The light that reaches us from most of the stars left many years ago. Perhaps radio and TV signals that we are sending out right now will be picked up on some distant planet or star in millions of years' time. Thousands of the stars we can see up in the sky are likely to no longer exist, having turned super-nova or collapsed into black holes millions of years ago. The light from those events may not reach our planet until long after the earth itself has been engulfed by the sun when it turns into a red giant in millions of years' time.

Relativity

Years ago people used to think that if we could travel at the speed of light it would solve all our space travel problems. But then the famous scientist, Albert Einstein, came along and invented the Theory of Relativity which says that it is impossible for anyone to travel at the speed of light because, among other things your mass would become infinite – you would become infinitely heavy!

This is something it would be best to avoid. We don't know what would happen to matter under these circumstances, but in theory all the matter in the universe would be attracted to you by your infinitely strong gravitational field and you might die and turn into a black hole.

Einstein also predicts many strange effects, including time dilation, for people who manage to travel close to the speed of light. The 'twin paradox' is probably the best known time dilation problem. If one twin, Fred, sets off at high speed (say around 99.5% of the speed of light) in a space ship, travels for some years, and then turns around and comes home at high speed to rejoin the other twin Mary, who stayed at home, he will arrive home many years younger than Mary, because his clocks have been running slower. For every ten years that Mary has aged, Fred will have aged only one year. If Fred was away for five years of his time, his twin sister would be fifty years older than him when he came back. Relativity says that a space ship exists in its own space-time continuum, so Fred wouldn't just look younger than Mary, he really would be younger, since time had been running slower for him. But how can time run at different speeds? Surely, time is time?

Time dilation has been proved by measuring the slowing down of the decay of sub-atomic particles called mesons when they have been accelerated to very high speed.

$e = mc^2$

Energy = mass x (speed of light^2)

This is Einstein's most famous equation, the equation of mass - energy equivalence. Einstein discovered that matter (the solid stuff the world and everything else is made of), and energy (heat & light etc), are one and the same thing. Matter is really just a form of super-compressed energy.

Looking at the equation above you can see that to work out how much energy something contains we must multiply its mass (weight) by the speed of light squared ($8.987551787368 \times 10^{16}$).

Thus the amount of energy that a small flower weighing just a gram contains is $1 \times 8.987551787368 \times 10^{16}$ joules (energy is measured in joules), or in non-scientific notation, 89,875,517,873,680,000 joules. That is easily enough energy to move the average mountain.

At the moment we can access only a tiny amount of the energy in matter, usually by burning it, but in years to come when we learn how to tap the energy in matter we should have an unlimited supply of cheap energy.

Paradoxical Problem

A paradox is a self-contradictory statement that is impossible to resolve like the 'twin paradox. Another paradoxical problem involves your family:

What would happen if you could go back in time and stop your own Grandmother from meeting your Grandfather?

If you could do that, you would never be born, but if you had never been born, how could you go back to the past? If you go, you weren't born, so you no longer exist, so you can't have stopped your grandmother from meeting your grandfather, so you're born, so you can go... Hence the paradox.

BINARY NUMBERS

Binary numbers are the language of computers and calculators, and consist only of ones and zeros. This is not instinctive or natural to humans but to computers binary notation is very simple. Computers can't really think, they can only put switches off or on. An off switch to a computer is a zero, an on switch is a one. When a computer looks at a number to see what it is, it really just looks to see what switches are on and off. In the same way, magnetic media and CDs record music and data as magnetic/not magnetic or reflective/not reflective. Most decisions we make in life can also be reduced to binary options. Up or down? Left or right? Forward or back? Yes or no? Better or worse? Hot or cold? Eat or not? Stay or go? Computers can also be taught to make such decisions, but they make their decisions based on the probability of success, from statistical data they have been fed. We humans use our judgement as it is not a good idea to base decisions on whether to cross the road on just the statistical probability of getting to the other side in one piece. It's better to look and cross when there is no traffic or to combine the ability to do that with a computer's ability to control the traffic.

Traffic lights use a simple binary code to operate. See if you can fill in the blanks on the diagram below, according to the following sequence (1) Red, (2) Red & Amber, (3) Green, (4) Amber, (5) Red. Red has been done for you to start off the sequence. Remember, 1 is on, 0 is off:

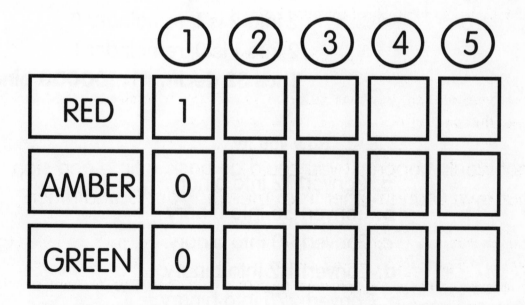

	①	②	③	④	⑤
RED	1				
AMBER	0				
GREEN	0				

Turn to page 112 for the answers ✔

Position value of binary numbers

The value of any position in a binary number doubles with each step to the left (1, 2, 4, 8, 16, 32 and so on). For example, 11011 in the binary number system means (1 x 16) + (1 x 8) + (0 x 4) + (1 x 2) + (1 x 1), which adds up to 27 in the decimal system.

Some calculators have a binary button which can be used to instantly convert numbers in decimal into binary, but it is also easy to do by hand.

Example:

Convert 32 into binary:

Solution method: Repeatedly divide 32 by 2, and write down the remainders. The final (last) remainder is the leftmost (first) digit of the binary.

2	32	remainder
	16	0
	8	0
	4	0
	2	0
	1	0

= 100000

Explanation:
2 into 32 is 16, remainder 0
2 into 16 is 6, remainder 0
2 into 8 is 4, remainder 0
2 into 4 is 2, remainder 0
2 into 2 is 1, remainder 0
2 into 1 is 0, remainder 1
Thus 32 decimal = 100000 binary

Now you try.

a. Convert 12 into binary.
b. Convert 56 into binary.
c. Convert 90 into binary.
d. Convert 112 into binary.
e. Convert 225 into binary.
f. Convert 450 into binary.

✔ *Turn to page 112 for the answers*

THE MAYAN NUMBER SYSTEM

The Mayan people lived in Central America over a thousand years ago and had a highly developed number system that was based around the vigesimal system (base 20). There are still Mayan people alive today but they no longer live in the great cities they once inhabited.

Among the advances they made, they pioneered the mathematical concept of zero, using the symbol: ⬤ This allowed them to express any whole number using place notation. In certain ways their numerical system was similar to the Roman system. But the Romans had no symbol for zero, so they had no place notation and long calculations were difficult. The Romans used a V for 5, and the Mayans used a line ▬▬ . The Romans used X for 10, but because the Mayans used the base 20, they don't have a single symbol for 10. They just put a five on top of another five. To write numbers over 20, the Mayans split their numbers into rows, with the numbers read vertically. To make 20 they put a dot above the zero symbol.

Below are the Mayan numerals for zero to 41. Here, after 19 the top row indicates the number of 20s, and the bottom row indicates the number of 1s or 5s. For example, the number 34 is made up from 20, 2 x 5, and 4 x 1. Use your logic to figure out the rest of the symbols up to 49, and fill in the blank boxes:

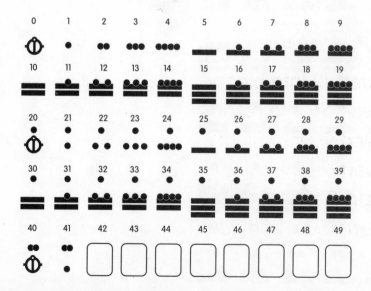

Turn to page 112 for the answers ✔

111

ANSWERS TO WOULD YOU BELIEVE IT

Binary Numbers:

	①	②	③	④	⑤
RED	1	1	0	0	0
AMBER	0	1	0	1	0
GREEN	0	0	1	0	0

a) 1100
b) 111000
c) 1011010
d) 1110000
e) 11100001
f) 111000010

The Mayan Number System:

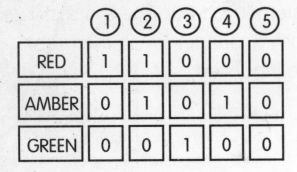